The Battle of the BULGE Cookbook

Gourmet Eating for the Diet-Conscious

by Selma Wassermann

drawings by Paula Snow

TARRAGON BOOKS
West Vancouver

dedicated with love to Jack, who taught me
about too much baking soda, among other things . . .

Design and typography by ees/The Typeworks
Printed in Canada by Hignell Printing Ltd., Winnipeg

Published by **TARRAGON BOOKS**
West Vancouver, British Columbia
V7W 1W8

CONTENTS

Individual recipes are listed at the beginning of each section.

A Call to Arms

This is a book of recipes for people who love to eat. It is also a book for people who, for a variety of medical or simple health considerations, have had to become diet-conscious.

For example—
. . . if you have had to watch while your friend stuffed a chocolate eclair into her size 10 face and you felt cheated because your own metabolism was thoroughly uncooperative, this book may be for you;
. . . if you have had to cut back drastically on your salt intake and felt that you could not ever enjoy food again, this book may be for you;
. . . if your doctor has told you to reduce your intake of saturated fats and cholesterol and you envisioned a permanent diet of cucumber sandwiches, this book may be for you;
. . . if you are diet-conscious, nutrition-conscious and health-conscious and believe that there is a delicious alternative to Escoffier cooking, this book may be for you;
. . . if you have, for the 12th time, shed those 20 pounds and this time you are determined to stay that way, this book may be for you.

Yes, Virginia, there *is* a way to reconcile your passion for food and your concerns about diet-conscious eating. You *can* eat elegant and mouth-watering food, *and* maintain your weight and cholesterol levels.

The on-going battle of the bulge rests on certain key principles of eating and food preparation. These few principles form the basis of all the recipes in this book. What's more, they are the very bedrock of a healthful diet. It would be important for you to be aware of them, and to use them in your day-to-day thinking about food, about weight maintenance and about sound nutrition.

Principles of Diet-Conscious Eating

♦ Eliminate refined sugar and refined-sugar foods from your diet. When you are cooking, substitute natural fruits for sugar to sweeten your food. **Alternatively,** use fructose or honey to sweeten foods. While they are still "fattening," these sweeteners do not have the same desctructive qualities as refined sugar.

♦ Reduce your intake of foods high in processed starch, such as white breads, cakes, pies, cookies, white rice. **Do eat some** starch—but make it count nutritionally by eating whole grains or whole wheat breads, or other high-fiber content foods.

♦ Eliminate prepared packaged foods, processed foods and any other foods that contain hidden carbohydrates and chemical preservatives. Start checking the contents of foods by reading what is stated on the labels of packages in the supermarket.

♦ Use corn oil margarine and corn oil primarily instead of butter and olive oil in your cooking. These latter should be used sparingly—and only when necessary.

♦ Reduce salt consumption drastically in all food preparations. Salt is an acquired taste and you can learn to de-acquire it.

♦ Increase your use of fresh vegetables and fresh fruits. Make sure that these foods are included daily in your diet.

♦ Reduce your consumption of high-fat meats. Use more veal, chicken and fish. Learn about tofu, the magic protein food.

♦ If you should be stricken with an attack of the "eats," indulge it in eating raw almonds, fresh fruit and fresh vegetable dishes.

♦ Never eat something you don't like just because you think it is going to be good for you.

♦ Food is to enjoy. Make every meal a pleasure. When you start feeling like a "victim" you may be tempted to comfort yourself by eating what is normally taboo.

♦ When following recipes from other cookbooks:

   a. reduce sugar ingredient by at least one-half; in time you will find that this is quite sweet enough,

   b. substitute honey or fructose for refined sugar,

   c. cut flour quantity by at least one-half; use whole wheat or graham flour whenever possible,

   d. substitute yogurt or buttermilk for sour cream,

   e. substitute milk or yogurt for heavy cream,

   f. substitute corn oil for olive oil; corn oil margarine or safflower oil margarine for butter.

But face it: your sauce will not be as rich when you use yogurt instead of heavy cream. Nevertheless, it will still be delicious and it will need no apologies.

◆   Keep your attention focused on the principles and do your own experimenting with substitutions in your favorite recipes. You'll be pleasantly surprised at how easy it is to adapt most recipes to the "battle of the bulge" way of eating.

I f you are a true lover of food and good eating, the diet you choose should allow for your continued pleasure in eating: it should not make you feel deprived and suffering. Your diet should allow you to eat so pleasurably that life feels worth living. Health and medical–diet considerations do not have to mean eating food that is tasteless and boring. The recipes in this book maintain the highest standards of excellence in taste, combined with calorie, carbohydrate, salt, cholesterol and saturated fat controls. They are easy to prepare. What's more, they reflect the nutritional concerns of people who, for medical or general health reasons, have become diet conscious.

Classification of the Recipes

The **Battle of the BULGE** is not for quick weight-loss diets. It deliberately avoids any cumbersome adherence to strict calorie counting and the weighing and measuring of portions. That approach is better left to the books which aim at substantial weight reduction. The **Battle of the BULGE** recommends a more subjective and common sense approach to encourage the waist-watcher to make his or her own thoughtful and informed judgments about what is best for his or her own dietary needs.

Each of the recipes in this collection has been included because it reflects a *reduction* in the amount of calories, carbohydrates and/or cholesterol we would normally ingest. However, it will become apparent that some recipes are more appropriate for calorie counters, while others are more suitable for cholesterol watchers. It should not be taken as a given that *all* recipes are appropriate to all kinds of dietary considerations.

To help readers through this maze, the following symbols will indicate which recipes are more appropriate to calorie-, cholesterol- and carbohydrate-reduced diets:

cal   *Recipes in which the per-portion calorie count is reduced*

carb   *Recipes in which the per-portion carbohydrate content is reduced*

chol   *Recipes in which the per-portion cholesterol intake is reduced*

In addition to these classifications, I have introduced another category, symbolized by this "Chef's Clock":

It identifies those recipes which require very little preparation time (30 minutes or less) and which can be put together with a minimum of fuss. While almost all of the recipes in the collection are relatively simple to prepare, those bearing the "Chef's Clock" will assure that your dinner will be on the table in less than one hour.

Abbreviations:

$t.$ = teaspoon
$T.$ = tablespoon
$c.$ = cup

SOUPS

Papaya Soup

Guests will beg for this recipe. It is an unbelievably delicious, scathingly easy-to-prepare cold soup. The secret ingredient is tequila. Olé!

Papayas, *4 large, peeled, seeded and cut in chunks*
Water, *3 c.*
Lemon, *juice of 1 whole*
Yogurt, *1 c.*
Tequila, *1/2 c.*
Triple Sec, *1/4 c.*
Lime, *thin slices for garnish*

Soups
◆
6

In a large saucepan, bring the papayas to a boil in the water and simmer for 5 minutes. Cool. ◆ Purée the papayas and the cooking liquid in a blender, along with the yogurt. Transfer to a large bowl. ◆ Add the tequila, the lemon juice and the triple sec and stir so that all the ingredients are blended. Chill. ◆ Serve with a thin slice of lime for garnish.

Serves 5-6.

Low in: **cal carb chol**

Cold Gazpacho

A simple but enthusiastic combination of fresh, crunchy vegetables that will enliven your summertime luncheons. A great dish for a low-calorie and low-cholesterol diet.

Purée the tomatoes, cucumbers, onion, green pepper and garlic in a blender or food processor. Pour into a large bowl.

♦**A**dd lemon juice, a few drops of Tabasco, tomato juice and oil. Add salt and pepper and stir until all ingredients are thoroughly blended.

♦**T**aste to correct seasoning. You may like a bigger "kick" and so may add more Tabasco. If you like it a little more sour, add a little more lemon juice. Chill and serve cold.

Serves 5-6.

*The key to this soup lies in getting the very best tomatoes. It's really not worth doing otherwise.

Low in: **cal carb chol**

6 large, ripe **Tomatoes***
2 peeled and seeded **Cucumbers**
1 large **Green Pepper**
1 large **Onion**
3-4 drops (to taste) **Tabasco**
1/4 c. **Corn Oil**
juice of 1 **Lemon**
2 c. **Tomato Juice**
no more than 1/2 t. **Salt**
(to taste) **Pepper**

Soups
♦
7

Cold Fruit Soup

The blend of fresh fruits with yogurt is a natural, and makes for a refreshing summer treat. You can vary the fruits, using what is locally available. But the banana is a must.

Raspberries, 2 c.
or **Strawberries,** 2 c.
Banana, 1
Peaches, 3 peeled
Apple, 1 peeled
Orange Juice, 2 c. unsweetened
Wine, 1 c. dry white
Yogurt, 1 c.
Cinnamon, 1 t.
Nutmeg, 1/2 t.
Fresh Mint, sprinkle (optional)

Soups

♦

8

Purée the fruit in a blender until smooth. (You can, of course, vary the fruit as you wish. You might consider plums, canteloupe, honeydew, papaya, mango, blueberries—and experiment with different combinations.)
♦ **P**lace fruit purée in a large bowl. Add wine and orange juice, cinnamon and nutmeg. Stir well. ♦ **T**aste to correct seasoning. You may sweeten further by adding more banana, or heighten cinnamon or nutmeg flavor. ♦ **W**hisk in yogurt until blended.
♦ **C**hill thoroughly and serve with a sprig of fresh mint, if desired.

Serves 5-6.

Low in: **cal chol**

Iced Dilled Cucumber Soup

You can feel quite virtuous as you indulge yourself in this delightful and refreshing and simple-to-prepare summer soup.

In your food processor or blender, chop the cucumber.
◆ **A**dd the mashed garlic and process one minute more.
◆ **P**lace the mixture in a large bowl and add the lemon rind and juice, the buttermilk, the yogurt, the chopped parsley and the dill weed. ◆ **M**ix all ingredients until thoroughly blended and add just a sprinkling of salt and freshly ground pepper to taste. Chill for several hours, because you want to serve this soup ice cold. Garnish with a few freshly chopped walnuts to really jazz it up.

Serves 4-6.

If English variety is unavailable, use 1 regular cucumber, peeled & seeded.

Low in: **cal chol carb**

1/2 peeled **English Cucumber,***
(you don't have to remove seeds)
2 cloves, mashed, **Garlic**
grated rind & juice, 1/2 **Lemon**
2 c. **Buttermilk**
2 c. **Yogurt**
3 T. *chopped fresh* **Parsley**
1 t. *dried* **Dillweed**
handful of chopped **Walnuts**

Soups
◆
9

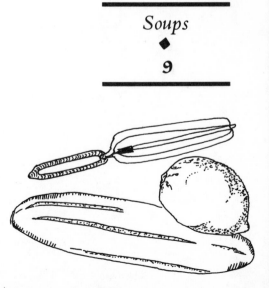

Cream of Cauliflower

This delightfully creamy soup needs no apologies for using yogurt and buttermilk instead of cream.

Corn Oil Margarine, *3 T.*
Onion, *1 large, minced*
Water, *4 c.*
Chicken Bouillon, *3 cubes*
Salt, *1 t.*
 (use less, but never more)
Cauliflower, *1 medium sized head, broken, or cut into pieces*
White Pepper, *1/2 t.*
Nutmeg, *1 t.*
Yogurt, *1 1/2 c.*

Soups

◆

10

In a saucepan, sauté the onion in the margarine until golden. Add the cauliflower pieces, water, bouillon cubes, salt and pepper and bring to a boil. Simmer for about 30 minutes. Cool slightly.   ◆**P**urée the soup in a blender or food processor, a little at a time, until smooth. Return the soup to the pot, stir in the yogurt and nutmeg, and heat gently, until warmed through. Do not boil, or yogurt will separate.   ◆**T**aste at this point to correct the seasoning. Serve warm, with a sprinkling of nutmeg on the top.   ◆**T**his can also be eaten as a cold soup with a dollop of yogurt as garnish.

Serves 5-6.

Low in: **cal carb chol**

Cream of Broccoli

The preparation is quite similar to the Cream of Cauliflower but the taste and eating experience are distincly different.

Discard the thick stalks at the bottom of the broccoli stem. Peel the rest of the stems and chop these, along with the flowerets. ◆ In a soup kettle, sauté the onions and garlic in the margarine, until the onions are golden. Add the bay leaf, allspice, pepper and thyme and stir for about one minute. ◆ Add the chopped broccoli, water, bouillon cubes and salt. Bring to a boil, cover and cook for about 15 minutes—until broccoli is tender. ◆ Remove the bay leaf and cool slightly. Purée in a blender or food processor until smooth. ◆ Return to pot and stir in the buttermilk and yogurt. Taste to correct seasoning. You may wish to add more pepper, or more thyme and/or allspice. Heat gently—but do not boil, or the yogurt will separate.

Serves 5-6.

1 large finely chopped **Onion**
1 clove minced **Garlic**
3 T. **Corn Oil Margarine**
1 bunch chopped **Broccoli**
1 t. **Salt**
(less if desired, but never *more)*
3 c. **Water**
2 cubes **Chicken Bouillon**
1 c. **Buttermilk**
1 c. **Yogurt**
1 **Bay Leaf**
1/2 t. **Allspice**
1/2 t. **White Pepper**
1/2 t. **Thyme**

Soups
◆
11

Low in: **cal chol carb**

Cream of Spinach

This exquisite potage à la florentine can be enjoyed with buttermilk instead of heavy cream, for half the calories.

Onion, *1 medium, chopped*
Corn Oil Margarine, *2 T.*
Spinach, *1 1/2 pounds fresh,*
  washed thoroughly and trimmed
  (or 10-oz. package frozen, defrosted)
Water, *4 c.*
Chicken Bouillon, *3 cubes*
Nutmeg, *1/2 t.*
Salt, *1/2 t.*
White Pepper, *a pinch*
Buttermilk, *1/2 c.*
Yogurt *for garnish (optional)*

Soups
◆
12

In a large enamel or stainless steel saucepan sauté the onion in the margarine until soft—about 5 to 8 minutes. ◆Squeeze the spinach dry and add to the pot, stirring to mix the spinach together with the onions. Cover and cook over low heat for about 5 minutes, stirring occasionally. ◆Add water and bouillon cubes and bring to a boil. Reduce heat, stir in nutmeg, salt and pepper and simmer over low heat for about 20 minutes. ◆When slightly cooled, purée in a blender or food processor, until smooth. Return to the pot and add buttermilk. Taste to correct seasoning, adding more pepper and nutmeg if desired. ◆This soup may be served hot or cold. You may wish to serve with a dollop of yogurt on top—which will increase the sourness.

Serves 5-6.

Low in: **cal carb chol**

Tomato Hot & Sour Soup

This is for the strong palate . . . for those who like their soups to curl their hair. Definitely for cold winter evenings!

In a soup kettle, sauté the onion and garlic in the margarine until the onion is soft.
◆ Add diced carrot and celery and stir for about 1 minute.
◆ Add tomatoes, tomato paste, water, chili flakes, vinegar, salt, pepper and dillweed. ◆ Bring to a boil. Reduce heat and simmer for about 30 minutes. Serve hot.

Serves 6-8.

* You can vary these amounts if you wish soup to be more or less hot/sour.

Low in: **cal carb chol**

3 T. **Corn Oil Margarine**
1 large diced **Onion**
2 cloves smashed **Garlic**
1 28-oz. can **Tomatoes**
1 can **Tomato Paste**
4, chopped fine, **Carrots**
3 stalks **Celery**
with leaves, chopped fine
7 c. **Water**
1/2 t. dried **Red Chili Flakes***
1/2 c. **White Vinegar***
1/2 t. **Salt**
1/2 t. freshly ground **Pepper**
1 t. **Dillweed**

Soups

◆

13

Zucchini Soup

Zucchini may be the most versatile vegetable in the garden. Low in calories, cholesterol & carbohydrate, high in nutrition, it can be used in an infinite variety of dishes.
Here it transforms itself into a succulent soup, to be served hot or cold.

Onions, *2 large, chopped fine*
Corn Oil, *2 T.*
Zucchini, *2 lbs., washed, trimmed, sliced in 1/2 inch pieces*
Chicken Stock, *4 c.*
Lemon Juice, *3 T.*
Potato, *1 small peeled and cut in quarters*
Garlic, *2 cloves, smashed*
Salt, *1/2 t. or less (never more)*
White Pepper, *1/2 t.*
Basil, *1 t. dried*
Yogurt *for garnish (optional)*

Soups
◆
14

In a saucepan, sauté the onions in the corn oil until soft.
◆ Add the zucchini, chicken stock, lemon juice, smashed garlic, salt and pepper and bring to a boil. ◆ Simmer, covered, for about 20 minutes. Let cool slighly. ◆ Purée in a blender or food processor.
◆ Taste to correct seasoning. Add more lemon juice, if you wish. Whether you serve the soup hot or cold, it may be garnished with a dollop of yogurt.

Serves 5-6.

Low in: **cal carb chol**

Mustard Green Soup "Hally" Locke

"Hally" Locke, a man of many talents, contributed this recipe for a light, gingery chicken-base soup. The recipe calls for boning a chicken, and using the bones for the stock —reserving the chicken meat for another recipe.

Soak mushrooms for about 30 minutes in hot water and slice very thin. ◆ **B**one the fryer and reserve the meat for another recipe. ◆ **P**ut 2 quarts of water, the chicken bones, feet and ginger in a large stainless or enamel pot. Bring to a boil, reduce heat and simmer for about 1 hour. Skim off any fat from the liquid. ◆ **S**train the broth and add bamboo shoots, mushrooms and liquid from the mushrooms, and water chestnuts. Simmer for another 10 minutes. ◆ **L**ast, add the mustard greens to the boiling broth. Cover and simmer for 4 minutes more. Greens should still be crisp. Serve immediately. Part of the success of this soup lies in the crispness of the vegetables, so be careful not to overcook them.

Serves 5-6.

Low in: **cal carb chol**

1 boned frying **Chicken**
2 quarts **Water**
3 slices fresh **Ginger**
1/4 c. **Bamboo Shoots**
3-4 dried **Chinese Mushrooms**
1/3 c. sliced **Water Chestnuts**
1/2 lb. chopped **Mustard Greens**

Soups
◆
15

Stracciatella (Italian Egg Drop Soup)

This incredibly easy soup provides a delightfully light and delicious beginning to any meal.
When the broth has been carefully de-fatted, the calorie count per serving is minimal. But the eggs and cheese make it somewhat tricky for cholesterol watchers.

Bring the soup to a boil.
◆ **B**eat the grated cheese into the beaten eggs. Add a little of the broth to the mixture and stir until smooth.   ◆ **D**ribble the egg mixture into the broth, beating with a fork for about 30 seconds.   ◆ **L**et the soup come barely to the boil again and serve immediately.

Serves 4-6.

*You may use home-made, thoroughly de-fatted broth, or an excellent quality canned broth.

Chicken Broth, * 1 quart
Eggs, 2, beaten
Grated Parmesan Cheese, 2 T.

Soups
◆
16

Low in: **cal carb**

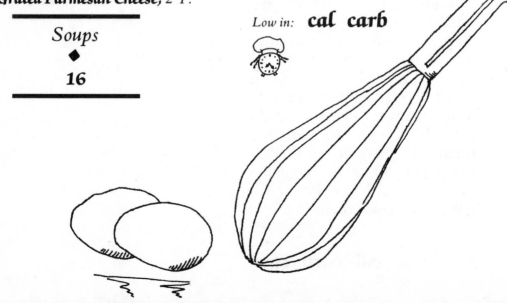

Carrot Orange & Yogurt Soup

The original recipe for this soup appears in Anne Thomas' The Vegetarian Epicure. *I have adapted it to conform to the diet principles of this book. A recipe definitely for those who like it hot!*

Melt the margarine in a large, heavy saucepan and sauté the onions and garlic until the onions are soft. ◆**A**dd the spices and cook on a low flame, for about 1 to 2 minutes more, stirring constantly. ◆**A**dd the carrots and the orange juice and stir until the spices are evenly dispersed in the mixture. ◆**A**dd the water, cover tightly and simmer for about 30 minutes. The carrots should be tender. Cool the soup slightly. ◆**P**urée the soup in a blender or food processor and return the purée to the saucepan. Beat in the yogurt with a whisk. ◆**H**eat soup, but do not allow it to boil, or yogurt will separate. Correct seasoning as desired. Garnish with chopped, fresh cilantro.**

Serves 5-6.

Low in: **cal chol**

3 T. **Corn Oil Margarine**
1 large chopped fine **Onion**
2 large cloves mashed **Garlic**
1/2 t. ground **Mustard***
1/2 t. ground **Trumeric***
1/2 t. ground **Ginger***
1/4 t. **Cayenne Pepper**
1/2 t. ground **Cumin***
1/2 t. **Cinnamon***
1/2 t. **Salt**
1 1/2 lbs. peeled and sliced **Carrots**
1/2 c. **Orange Juice**
grated rind of one **Orange**
4 c. **Water**
2 c. **Yogurt**
to taste, **Black Pepper**
fresh, chopped **Cilantro****

Soups

◆

17

*If you like things spicy, use heaping 1/2-teaspoon measures, instead of level, of each of the spices marked.

**See note at bottom of next page.

Mushroom Soup Bangkok

If you've never tried Thai cooking, this recipe may be a good introduction. Simple to prepare, low in calories, with a perfectly exquisite blend of flavors. For those who like it HOT!

Corn Oil, *2 T.*
Garlic, *3 cloves, smashed*
Red Chili Peppers,
  *1/2 t. dried, crushed**
Coriander, *1/2 t. ground*
Chicken Stock,* 6 c.*
Fresh Mushrooms,
  1/2 lb., quartered
Soya Sauce, *1 t.*
Fresh Cilantro,** *5-6 sprigs,*
  chopped (use stems and leaves)

Soups
◆
18

Heat the oil in a saucepan and add the smashed garlic, chili peppers, and ground coriander. Saute for 1 minute. ◆**A**dd the chicken stock and bring to a boil. ◆**A**dd soya sauce and fresh mushrooms. Bring to a boil again and simmer for 2 minutes more. Turn off heat. ◆**T**hrow in the chopped cilantro and serve immediately.

Serves 4-6.

* *Reduce this to 1/4 t. if you prefer a less zesty "bite."*

** *Use chicken bouillon cubes, a good quality canned chicken broth, or thoroughly de-fatted home-made stock.*

*** *Cilantro, or Chinese parsley, is the leaf and stalk of the coriander plant. We get our cilantro from the produce markets of Chinatown. You can, of course, grow your own if you're so inclined . . . but start now if you want this soup by next spring.*

Low in: **cal carb chol**

SALADS

Broccoli & Roasted Pepper Salad

This large raw-vegetable salad is a meal in itself. The vegetables may vary, but absolutely essential is the broccoli-roasted pepper combination. Nothing to cook, and wonderfully healthful for you; a dieter's delight.

1 small bunch **Broccoli**
1 small **Onion**
sliced thin and rings separated
1/2 small jar **Roasted Peppers**
cut in strips
2 **Carrots**
trimmed, scraped and sliced
1 ripe **Avocado**
cut in bite-size pieces
1/4 c. toasted **Sunflower Seeds**
1/4 c. **Corn Oil**
1/4 c. **Wine Vinegar**
1 t. **Mustard Powder**
1 large clove mashed **Garlic**
1/4 t. **Salt**
freshly ground **Pepper**

Trim bottom of broccoli stems. Peel skin from stalks and cut stalks and flowerets into bite-sized pieces.
◆ **C**ombine all raw vegetables and sunflower seeds in a large bowl. ◆ **M**ake a dressing by combining the corn oil, wine vinegar, mustard powder, garlic, salt and pepper. Mix or shake well. ◆ **A**dd dressing to salad and toss well. (This salad will keep nicely for several hours, marinating in the dressing. Only the seeds go limp, so if you are going to prepare it ahead of time, seeds should be added at the last minute.)

Serves 5-6.

Low in: **cal carb chol**

Raw Mushroom Salad

This simple mushroom salad has a middle-eastern orientation. It is a lovely and delicate salad accompaniment to almost any entrée.

Mushrooms, *1 lb. raw, cleaned sliced in quarters (use stems, too)*
Garlic, *1 clove, minced*
Parsley, *2 T. chopped fresh*
Salt, *1/4 t.*
Pepper, *freshly ground, to taste*
Basil, *1/2 t. dried*
Oregano, *1/2 t. dried*
Corn Oil, *2 T.*
Lemon Juice, *2 T.*

Salads

◆

22

Combine the mushrooms, garlic, parsley, herbs and seasonings in a medium- sized bowl. ◆**T**oss with oil and lemon juice until thoroughly blended. Chill and serve.

Serves 3-4.

Low in: **cal carb chol**

Broccoli Mushroom Salad

Raw vegetable salads are most satisfying main-dish lunches for ardent waist-watchers. Try this broccoli-mushroom combination — it provides a lot of munching and crunching without worrying about consequences.

Cut off thick bottom end of each broccoli stalk and discard. Peel skin from the rest of the stalk. Slice stalks and the flowerets into bite-sized pieces. ◆ Combine all raw vegetables and blend with the smashed garlic. ◆ Add oil, vinegar, spices and seasonings and toss very well. ◆ Chill for 1 to 2 hours. This salad is much nicer when it has been marinating in the dressing for a while.

Serves 5-6.

Low in: **cal carb chol**

1 medium bunch fresh **Broccoli**
1/2 lb. fresh **Mushrooms**
washed and sliced
1 large sliced **Onion**
with rings separated
2 cloves smashed **Garlic**
1 **Green Pepper**
cut in strips
1 can **Water Chestnuts**
drained and sliced
1/4 c. **Wine Vinegar**
1 t. **Mustard Powder**
1 t. powdered **Ginger**
1/4 t. **Salt**
freshly ground, to taste, **Pepper**
1/4 c. **Corn Oil**

Salads
◆
23

Ensalada de Nopales

You will stymie and titillate your guests with this exceptional and exceptionally simple-to-prepare cactus salad — a new taste and texture, and a swell beginning to a special dinner.

Cactus,* *1 jar*
Onion, *1 small, diced fine*
Cilantro, *1/2 bunch*
 leaves and stems, chopped fine
Corn Oil, *2 T.*
Wine Vinegar, *2 T.*
Tabasco, *3-4 drops (or to taste)*
Iceberg Lettuce, *1/4 head, shredded*
Green Onions, *2-3*
 chopped for garnish

Salads
◆
24

Put the nopales (cactus) in a colander and rinse several times. Drain thoroughly.
◆ **O**n a large serving platter, make a bed of shredded lettuce.   ◆ **M**ix together the cactus, onion, cilantro, corn oil, vinegar and Tabasco. Place on top of the lettuce.   ◆ **G**arnish with a sprinkling of green onion. Chill and serve.

Serves 5-6.

**Marinated cactus (nopales) is found in jars in Mexican markets or in those markets which cater to specialty food interests.*

Low in: **cal carb chol**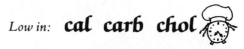

Zucchini Slaw

New recipes often rise, like a Phoenix, from the ashes of disappointment over missing ingredients. So did this Zucchini Slaw emerge when we wanted slaw —with no cabbage in sight. Rather than a second cousin, it stands firmly as a preferred choice. Cut calories and cholesterol by substituting yogurt for half the usual amount of mayonnaise.

Trim the zucchini, scrub the skins and grate them coarsely. Place the grated zucchini in a colander with a plate on top. Top with a heavy weight and allow pressure to draw off excess liquid for at least 30 minutes. ◆ **G**rate the onion.
◆ **C**ombine the zucchini and onion with the seasonings and herbs. ◆ **M**ix the mayonnaise, yogurt and vinegar in a small bowl, until blended.
◆ **S**tir this dressing into the zucchini and chill before serving. Like other slaws, this salad retains its goodness for several days.

Serves 5-6.

Low in: **cal carb**

4 large **Zucchini**
1 **Onion**
1/2 t. (or to taste) **Salt**
freshly ground **Pepper**
1 T. dried **Basil**
1/2 c. **Mayonnaise**
1/2 c. **Yogurt**
1/4 c. **Vinegar**

Salads

◆

25

Crudités

Pass up the potato chips & peanuts and settle for a platter of crudités —munchy, crunchy raw vegetables with low-calorie dips to increase your eating pleasure & not your belt size.

Good raw vegetable options for crudités:

Cherry Tomatoes	**Celery sticks**	**Cucumber slices**
Broccoli flowerets	**Small, whole**	**Radishes**
Carrot sticks	**Mushrooms**	**Green Onions**
Cauliflower flowerets	**Jerusalem Artichoke**	**Fennel slices**
Zucchini sticks	**slices**	**Jicama slices**

Low-Cal Dips

These simple dips are best mixed in a blender for a smoother, creamier consistency:

1

1 c. low-fat Cottage Cheese
1/4 c. Yogurt
1 clove Garlic

2

1 c. Cottage Cheese
1/4 c. Yogurt
1/4 c. Blue Cheese

3

1 c. Cottage Cheese
1/4 c. Yogurt
1 clove Garlic
4 Anchovy filets

Low in: **cal carb chol**

Salads

◆

26

Antipasto

Those wonderful Italians had a great idea when they arranged these salad ingredients into a visual and culinary fantasy.

On a very large serving platter, place the following ingredients into mix–and–match groups:

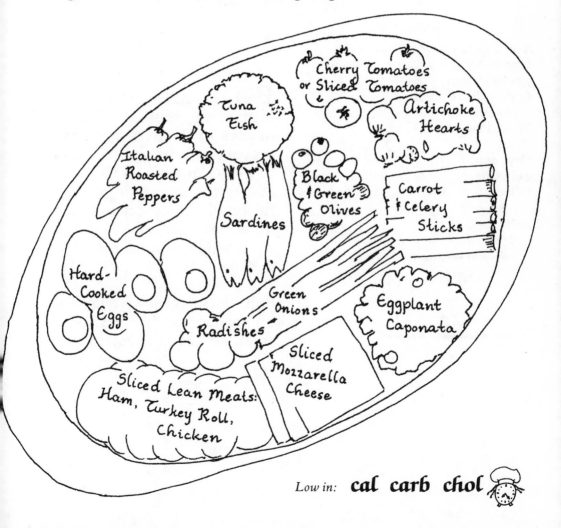

Low in: **cal carb chol**

Famous Greek Salad

Everybody's eating Greek salad these days and I can easily understand why. Here's a simple-to-prepare recipe that will serve as a light, bulge-battling dish.

Tomatoes, *4 large*
Cucumber, *1 large*
Green Pepper, *1 large*
Onion, *1 medium sized*
Corn Oil, *2 T.*
Wine Vinegar, *2 T.*
Basil, *1 t.*
Oregano, *1/2 t.*
Feta Cheese, *1/4 lb., crumbled*
Olives, *6-8 Greek or Italian (optional)*
Salt, *1/4 t.*
Pepper, *freshly ground, to taste*

Salads

◆

28

Peel cucumber. Cut it and pepper in chunks. Cut tomatoes in quarters and again crosswise in halves. Peel and thin-slice onion. ◆**C**ombine all vegetables in a large, colorful bowl. (Add tomatoes last otherwise they tend to get squashed by other vegetables.) ◆**A**dd oil, vinegar, spices and seasonings and toss lightly. ◆**S**prinkle feta chese on top and add olives, if desired. Serve immediately.

Serves 4-6.

Low in: **cal carb chol**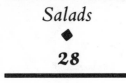

Fruit Salad with Yogurt & Nuts

This is, without question, one of my all-time favorite summer lunch specials. Vary the fruits to your own taste and produce this wonderfully simple and beautiful dish.

Some fruit options:

Apple	Pineapple	Honeydew
Grapefruit	Banana	Strawberries
Orange	Peach	Mango
Papaya	Canteloupe	

Some nut options:

Raw Almonds	Sunflower	Unsalted
Walnuts	seeds	Macadamia

Cut fruits up in bite-size pieces. ◆**A**rrange on individual platters. ◆**P**lace a dollop of plain yogurt on the top of the fruit. ◆**S**prinkle with 1 T. nuts of your choice.

Low in: **cal chol**

Caesar Salad

This salad is an old favorite that still shines — even without the added carbohydrates of croutons. Corn oil quite easily substitutes for the normally-called-for olive oil — and waist-watchers will not suffer sorely from such an exchange.

Romaine Lettuce, *1 large head*
Garlic, *1 large clove, smashed*
Corn Oil, *2 T.*
Wine Vinegar, *3 T.*
Grated Parmesan Cheese, *2-3 T.*
Worcestershire Sauce, *1/2 t.*
Dry Mustard, *1 t.*
Black Pepper, *1 t. freshly ground*
Anchovies, *4 filets, mashed*

Salads

◆

30

Wash and spin-dry lettuce, and tear into small pieces. ◆ In a large salad bowl, place mashed garlic and add oil and vinegar. Beat with a fork until blended. ◆ **A**dd Worcestershire sauce, cheese, mustard and anchovies and beat again until blended. ◆ **A**dd lettuce leaves and toss, until all leaves are coated with dressing — taking care not to bruise leaves. ◆ **L**ast, grind about 1 t. black pepper over the salad and serve. (You may want to sprinkle a little more of the Parmesan cheese on top.)

Serves 3-4.

Low in: **cal carb chol**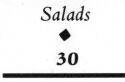

Korean Bean Sprout Salad

This is a light and refreshing salad accompaniment to most entrées — but I like it best with fish. It takes only minutes to prepare and the presence of the sesame seeds makes for a wonderful taste surprise.

Toss the bean sprouts with the green onions to mix.
◆ In a blender, combine the oil, vinegar, soya sauce, sesame seeds, and garlic and purée until the seeds are pulverized. Pour this dressing over the sprouts and toss. Chill and serve.

Serves 3-4.

Low in: **cal carb chol**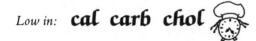

2 T. **Corn Oil**
2 T. **Wine Vinegar**
2 T. **Soya Sauce**
1/2 t. **Black Pepper**
freshly ground
2 T. **Sesame Seeds**
1 clove, smashed, **Garlic**
1 lb. fresh **Bean Sprouts**
washed and drained
2 chopped **Green Onions**

Salads
◆
31

Two Kinds of Cucumber Salad

These salads are best made when cucumbers are absolutely excellent in flavor. Both of these recipes are incredibly simple, low in calories and wonderfully delicious salad accompaniments.

CUCUMBER SALAD I:

Cucumbers, *2*
Onion, *1 medium-sized*
Vinegar, *1/4 c.*
Water, *1/4 c.*
Salt, *1/4 t.*
Pepper, freshly ground
Dillweed, *1/2 t.*

CUCUMBER SALAD II:

Cucumbers, *2*
Yogurt, *1 c. plain*
Garlic, *1 clove chopped fine*
Corn Oil, *1 t.*
Salt, *1/4 t.*
Fresh Mint, *1 T.*

Salads

◆

32

Cucumber Salad I:

Peel and slice cucumbers very thin. Place in a small bowl. ◆**A**dd thinly sliced onion. ◆ **M**ix vinegar with water and salt. Add to cucumbers and toss. ◆**A**dd freshly ground pepper and dillweed. Toss again. ◆**C**hill and serve.

Cucumber Salad II:

Peel and slice cucumbers very thin. Place in a small bowl. ◆**A**dd yogurt, salt, garlic, corn oil and mint. ◆**T**oss, chill and serve.

Serves 3-4.

*If fresh unavailable, use 1 t. dried.

Low in: **cal carb chol**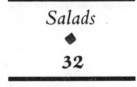

Parsley Salad

Parsley is usually thought of as a garnish, and even discarded by most diners. Try making it into a salad of its own, for a delightfully different and nourishing eating experience.

2 bunches of **Parsley**
absolutely fresh
4 cloves, chopped fine, **Garlic**
1 medium, chopped fine, **Onion**
3 large, chopped fine, **Tomatoes**
2 T. **Corn Oil**
2 T. **Lemon Juice**
1/2 t. **Salt**
freshly ground, to taste, **Pepper**

Salads

◆

33

cal

carb

chol

Wash and drain the parsley and trim the stems off. Chop until very, very fine. ◆ **M**ix the chopped parsley with the chopped onion, garlic and to-matoes. ◆ **T**oss lightly with the corn oil, lemon juice, salt and pepper. Chill and serve.

Serves 3-4.

Bean Sprout & Cilantro Salad

The crunchiness of the bean sprouts with the uplifting flavor of fresh cilantro* makes a different salad combination. The very low calorie count turns it into a waist-watcher's special. What's more, the entire dish takes about 8 seconds to prepare!

Bean Sprouts, *1 lb. fresh*
Cilantro, **1 bunch fresh*
Green Onions, *2 large, thin-sliced*
Garlic, *1 small clove, smashed*
Salt, *1/8 t.*
Pepper, *freshly ground, to taste*
Corn Oil, 2 T.
Wine Vinegar, *2 T.*

Salads

◆

34

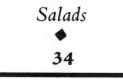

Wash the bean sprouts and drain them thoroughly.
◆**W**ash and drain the cilantro and chop it coarsely.
◆**C**ombine the bean sprouts, cilantro, green onions and garlic. ◆**S**prinkle with seasonings, oil and vinegar and toss lightly until blended. Chill and serve.

Serves 3-4.

**See note at bottom of page 18.*

Low in: **cal chol carb**

Mixed Green Salad

Green salads —a standby for dedicated waist-watchers —can grow boring unless you create interest by using a variety of different house dressings. Treat yourself to one of these delicious alternatives to plain oil and vinegar.

Try mixing some of these "greens":

Romaine lettuce, iceberg lettuce, red lettuce, butter lettuce, spinach, green onions, radish, Jerusalem artichoke, celery, carrot, cucumber, zucchini, broccoli flowerets, cauliflower flowerets, mushrooms, fennel, bean sprouts, alfalfa sprouts, cabbage, daikon radish, jicama.

Each of the following "house dressings" will dress 2 to 3 portions of salad:

I: Tangy

4 T. **Corn Oil**
3 T. **Wine Vinegar**
1 clove **Garlic,** smashed
1/2 t. **Worcestershire Sauce**
1/2 t. **Mustard Powder**
1/4 t. **Salt**
freshly ground **Pepper**

Combine and shake or beat well.

II: Garlic

2 cloves **Garlic,** smashed
4 T. **Corn Oil**
3 T. **Wine Vinegar**
1/4 t. **Salt**
freshly ground **Pepper**

Combine and shake well.

III: Creamy Avocado & Garlic

1 ripe **Avocado,** mashed
4 T. **Corn Oil**
4 T. **White Vinegar**
1 small **Onion**
2 cloves **Garlic**
1/4 t. **Salt**
black **Pepper**
1/2 bunch **Parsley** tops (no stems)
1/4 c. **Water**

Mix in blender or food processor.

IV: Interesting & New: Tahini

1 clove **Garlic**
1/2 t. **Salt**
1/2 c. **Tahini**
1/2 c. **Water**
1/2 c. **Lemon Juice**

Mix in blender or food processor. Thin with more water and/or lemon juice if desired.

Low in: **cal carb chol**

Tomato Salad with Onions & Basil

Tomatoes and onions are sprinkled with basil and oregano to heighten flavor and create new interest in a wonderful old-favorite salad.

Beefsteak Tomatoes
   4-5 large, sliced
Bermuda Onion, *1 large, very thinly sliced*
Oregano, *1/2 t. dried*
Fresh Basil, *6-8 leaves*
Corn Oil, *2 T.*
Wine Vinegar, *2 T.*
Blue Cheese, *2 T. crumbled (optional)*
Salt, *1/4 t.*
Fresh Pepper, *to taste*

Salads

◆

36

Arrange the slices of tomatoes on a large platter, with the slices of onion on the top. Place basil leaves strategically between onion and tomato slices. This could look like a work of art.   ◆**S**prinkle the oil and vinegar over the top and then the herbs and seasonings.   ◆**Y**ou will want to serve this immediately, since cut tomatoes are not good at waiting.

Serves 3-4.

Low in: **cal chol carb**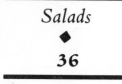

BIRD & BEAST ENTRÉES

Barcelona Workers-Style Chicken

This recipe comes from a tiny working-class restaurant in Barcelona. Don't be put off by the quantity of garlic. You'll be surprised and pleased at what happens to the garlic when it is cooked with its skin on. But the dish is definitely for garlic lovers only.

Dry each piece of chicken thoroughly. This is very important if the chicken is to brown. Sauté the chicken pieces in the 2 T. corn oil, until each piece is nicely browned. Medium to high heat will help this process and if your pan is too small, you may have to do it in two lots. ◆**A**dd the garlic cloves, *skin on.* Yes. Add them all. Keep the flame medium-high, and continue the sauté, for several minutes more, until the garlic skins turn shiny. ◆**N**ow, pour off all the excess fat from the pan—there will be a lot more than when you started, as the chicken will have lost its own fat in the process. Make sure you get all the fat out. ◆**A**dd 1/2 c. vinegar, salt and pepper to taste, and cover the pan. Reduce the heat and simmer, stirring occasionally, for about 15 minutes.

Serves 4-5.

Low in: **cal carb chol**

1 fryer **Chicken**
cut up in small pieces
2 T. **Corn Oil**
1 whole head of **Garlic**
(about 20-30 cloves)
1/2 c. **White Vinegar**
1/2 t. **Salt**
freshly ground, to taste, **Pepper**

Bird
& Beast
39

Chicken in the Greek Manner

Incredibly simple to prepare, your efforts result in a lemony-roasted chicken, with a sprinkling of piquant herbs to add vital interest in the eating.

Chicken, *small roaster, 3-4 pounds*
Corn Oil Margarine, *2 T.*
Garlic, *3 cloves, smashed*
Basil, *1 t.*
Oregano, *1 t.*
Salt, *1/4 t.*
Black Pepper, *freshly grated, to taste*
Lemons, *juice of 2*
  grated rind of 1

---

*Bird
& Beast*
40

Pre-heat the oven to 400°. Put the margarine with the garlic in the roasting pan and place it in the oven. Keep your eye on the pan until the margarine has melted and the garlic is browned. Remove the pan from the oven. ◆ **D**ip a pastry brush into the margarine-garlic, and brush this mixture all over the chicken. Remove excess fat from the roasting pan. Place chicken in the pan, and put it into the hot oven for 30 minutes—or until it begins to brown. ◆ **R**emove chicken from the pan. Pour off excess fat. Add herbs, pepper, lemon juice and grated rind to the pan. Turn the chicken in this mixture several times so that it is doused in this lemon juice and herb bath. ◆ **R**eturn the chicken to the oven. Lower the heat to 325° and cook, covered, for one hour more.

Serves 4-5.

Low in: **cal carb chol**

Chicken Curry with Yogurt

Chicken marries yogurt in this mild, aromatic and flavorful curry.

Sauté the onion and the garlic in the oil until the onions are soft. Add the chicken and brown on all sides. ◆ **Re**move chicken and drain off any excess chicken fat that has accumulated in the pan. ◆ **A**dd the spices. Stir until thoroughly blended. Add tomatoes and mix well. Return the chicken to the pan, cover, and lower the heat. Cook for 45 minutes. ◆ **U**ncover the pan, raise the heat and cook until the sauce is reduced. Add the yogurt last, and heat thoroughly, but do not boil.

Serves 4-5.

Low in: **cal carb chol**

1 cut up frying **Chicken**
2 T. **Corn Oil**
2 chopped **Onions**
2 cloves minced **Garlic**
1/4 t. **Salt**
freshly ground **Pepper**
1 t. **Turmeric**
1 t. ground **Coriander**
1 t. **Cumin**
2 t. **Curry Powder**
2 whole **Cloves**
1/2 **Cinnamon Stick**
1 **Bay Leaf**
a pinch of **Thyme**
1 small can of **Stewed Tomatoes**
1/2 c. **Yogurt**

Bird & Beast
41

Roasted Chicken à l'Orange

Pass the high-fat duck in favor of the chicken and you will find this orange juice, soya sauce and garlic bath doing miracles for the more mundane bird.

Orange Juice, *1 c.*
Soya Sauce, *1 c.*
Garlic, *4 large cloves, smashed*
Ground Ginger, *1 t.*
Mustard Powder, *1 t.*
Chicken, *3-1/2-4 lb. roaster with all fat trimmed off*

Bird
& Beast
42

Mix the orange juice, the soya sauce, the garlic, the ginger and the mustard powder together and place these in a large dish. Place the whole chicken in this aromatic bath for a 24 hour period, during which time you must turn the chicken several times, so that all sides are evenly marinated. This sit-in-the-bath stage should take place in the refrigerator. ◆ **D**rain the chicken, put it in a roasting pan and place in a pre-heated, 400° oven for about 20 minutes — or until the outside skin becomes nicely browned. Then turn the oven down to 300° and roast the bird for one hour more.

Serves 4-5.

Low in: **cal chol**

Chicken with Cilantro

The delightfully fresh flavor of cilantro* gives a cooling and refreshing taste to meats and vegetables. In this recipe, cilantro balances with the garlic and pepper, making for an unusual hot-cool flavor experience.

Mix the salt, crushed garlic, ground pepper and lemon juice together. Wash and chop the cilantro, and add to the garlic mixture. Blend, until you have a smooth paste. ◆ **R**ub the paste into the pieces of chicken. Place the chicken in a dish, cover it over with plastic wrap, and refrigerate for several hours, or overnight. ◆ **P**re-heat the oven to 350° and bake the chicken pieces for about one hour. Alternatively, if you have an outdoor barbecue, you may grill this chicken over hot coals with excellent results.

Serves 4-5.

*See note at the bottom of page 18.

Low in: **cal carb chol**

1 small roasting **Chicken**
cut into pieces
6 (yes, 6) cloves of **Garlic**
smashed
1/2 t. **Salt**
2 T. crushed or ground **Black Pepper**
5-6 sprigs of fresh **Cilantro***
(use leaves and stems)
2 T. **Lemon Juice**

Bird
& Beast
43

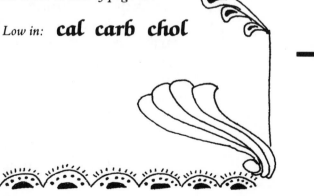

Chicken Saté

The saté, from Indonesia, gives us a different taste experience —definitely for those who prefer hot and spicy eating.

Soya Sauce, *1/4 c.*
Orange Juice, *1/4 c.*
Corn Oil, *2 T.*
Red Peppers,
  1/2 t. dried crushed
Garlic, *1 clove, crushed*
Peanut Butter, *1/4 c.*
Onion, *2 T. minced*
Coriander, *1 t. ground*
Turmeric, *1 t.*
Ginger, *1/2 t. ground*
Chicken Breasts, *2*
  skin and bone removed

Bird
& Beast
44

Make a marinade of the first 10 ingredients and mix these well. ◆ **C**ut the breasts into 1-inch pieces and stir these into the marinade so that they are all equally anointed with the liquid. Marinate in the refrigerator for 3 hours. ◆ **S**oak wooden skewers in warm water for about 5 minutes. This will prevent them from burning while broiling the meat. Thread the chicken on the skewers—but do not crowd the pieces too tightly together. ◆ **B**roil about 2 inches from the broiler flame, until done on all sides. This may require turning 2 to 3 times. ◆ **Y**ou may wish to warm the marinade and serve this as a sauce over the chicken. While excellent, it does increase the spiciness of the taste.

Serves 4-5.

Low in: **cal chol carb**

Josephine's Chicken Chablis

*Fresh sage,
if you can get it,
makes this dish perfect.
If not, dry sage is acceptable
—but not quite the same.*

In a heavy skillet, melt the margarine and place the chicken pieces so that they all just fit. (If your skillet is too small, you might have to do the chicken in two lots.) Brown the chicken over a high flame, on all sides.   ◆**W**hen all the chicken is browned, pour off excess fat from pan.   ◆**A**dd the salt, pepper and sage. Raise heat, and add 1/2 cup of wine. Cook over this high flame, with your careful attention, turning the chicken over and over in the wine. The chicken will gratefully soak this up.
◆**T**hen add more wine and turn the chicken about two times more. Keep adding wine as chicken soaks it up, until the half bottle has been used. This should take about 30 minutes and the chicken should be tender to the fork when the last of the wine has been absorbed.
◆**G**arnish the chicken with the wine-soaked sage leaves.

Serves 4-5.

Low in: **carb chol**

4 T. **Corn Oil Margarine**
1 fryer, quartered, **Chicken**
fresh whole **Sage**
10-12 leaves, or more
1/4 t. **Salt**
freshly ground, to taste, **Pepper**
1/2 bottle **Dry White Wine**
(e.g. Chablis)

*Bird
& Beast*
45

Chicken Tikkas

Chicken tikkas is originally a Pakistani dish, traditional to that country. This recipe is modified in accord with the diet principles of this book. I think you will not noticeably suffer in the eating from these substitutions.

Fryer, 1
cut up into serving pieces
Yogurt, 1 c.
Garlic, 2 cloves, smashed
Onion, 1 small minced
Cinnamon, 1/2 t.
Cumin Powder, 1 t.
Black Pepper, 1/2 t. fresh-ground
Cardamom, 1/2 t. ground
Ginger, 1/2 t. powdered
Cloves, 1/4 t. powdered
Nutmeg, 1/4 t.
Cayenne Pepper, 1/2 t.
Salt, 1/4 t.

OPTIONAL SAUCE:

Yogurt, 1 c.
Garlic, 1 clove, minced
Mint Leaves, chopped
1 T. dried or 1/2 c. fresh

Bird
& Beast
46

Make a marinade by mixing together all the ingredients except for the chicken. Place the chicken pieces into the marinade and refrigerate, in a covered dish, overnight. It is always a good idea to turn the chicken around, several times, so that it is evenly bathed.
◆ **R**emove the chicken from marinade and place on a broiling tray. Broil, slowly, on all sides, until very brown. (Even more delicious when it can be done on a charcoal grill.)
◆ **W**hen serving, you may wish to dip the chicken in a sauce made by mixing the indicated ingredients. However, the chicken can well stand on its own merit, and the sauce is truly optional.

Serves 4-5.

Low in: **cal chol carb**

Elaine's Wonderful Instant Chicken for Sixty

Elaine Block invented this magic recipe which she uses to entertain large groups of guests for dinner. It is incredibly easy and incredibly delicious, with calories and carbohydrates carefully controlled. The amounts in the recipe below should serve 3 to 4. Increase quantities proportionally if you are planning to test the recipe on the multitudes.

Dip each piece of chicken into the melted margarine, then into the cheese. ◆ **P**lace chicken on a rack, in a roasting pan, and bake in a pre-heated 375° oven, for 1 hour. (The chicken should turn brown and crusty on top, and does not have to be turned during the cooking.) ◆ **T**hat's all there is to it! (This magic recipe can be made a day in advance and simply heated the next day with no noticeable loss in flavor.)

Low in: **cal carb**

1 cut up frying **Chicken**
2 melted T. **Corn Oil Margarine**
1/2 c. grated **Parmesan Cheese**

*Bird
& Beast
47*

Roasted Turkey —Stuffed with Panache

This all-vegetable stuffing not only holds the calories down, it is a delicious alternative to any of the high carbohydrate/calorie kinds, & will win you applause for craftspersonship as well as creativity.

STUFFING:

Onion, *1 large, diced*
Garlic, *2 cloves, chopped*
Corn Oil, *2 T.*
Celery, *2 stalks, chopped*
Green Pepper, *1 small, chopped*
Mushrooms, *1/2 lb. fresh, sliced*
Water Chestnuts, *1 small can drained and sliced*
Turkey Liver & Gizzard, *diced*
Marjoram, *1/2 t.*
Sage, *1/2 t.*
Thyme, *1/2 t.*
Salt, *1/4 t.*
Pepper, *freshly ground, to taste*

Prepare the stuffing first. Sauté the onion and garlic in the corn oil for 6 to 8 minutes, or until the onion turns golden. Add the celery, green pepper, and turkey giblets, and continue the sautée for 10 minutes more. ◆**A**dd the mushrooms and all the seasonings, and continue cooking for another 15 to 20 minutes. Finally, add the water chestnuts and cook for 5 minutes more. Taste at this stage to correct the seasoning. Allow to cool.

(continued) *Now turn your attention to the bird —*

Stuff the turkey tightly with the stuffing mixture and truss the bird so that the stuffing is secure. A little of the stuffing juices will leak out, but this just adds to the flavor of the roasting juices in the pan.

♦ **M**ix the orange juice with the sherry and pour this all over the bird, allowing excess to drain into the roasting pan. Sprinkle garlic powder over the bird, generously, if you like a good garlic-flavored skin, or lightly, if you prefer less of a garlic accent.

♦ **R**oast the turkey in a 350° oven, for about 2 1/2 to 3 hours, basting every 30 minutes with the orange sherry sauce. You will want to turn the turkey once during the cooking, so that it will brown evenly. But make sure you let it sit outside the oven for about 20 minutes before carving. Carving when the bird is too hot results in slicing difficulties and poor-looking pieces of meat.

Low in: **cal carb chol**

TURKEY:

1 10-12 lb. **Turkey**
1 c. **Orange Juice**
1/2 c. **Dry Sherry**
Garlic Powder

*Bird
& Beast*
49

Roulade of Beef

This is a variation of a recipe for Paupiette de Boeuf which I have adapted according to the diet principles of this book. None of the guests to whom I've served it has complained about the renovation and the dish has become a favorite in its own right.

Beef, *4-6 thin slices*

STUFFING:

Onion, *4 T., minced*
Garlic, *2 cloves, minced*
Thyme, *1 t.*
Parsley, *3 T. fresh, chopped*
Black Pepper, *freshly grated*

SAUCE:

Carrots, *2, cut in dice*
Tomatoes, *2-3 large, chopped*
Onion, *1 large, minced*
Corn Oil, *2 T.*
Beef Bouillon Cube, *1*
Dry White Wine, *1 c.*

Mix the stuffing ingredients together and spread each beef slice with a little of this mixture. Roll and pin with a toothpick.   ◆ In a large frying pan, sauté the onion in the oil until quite brown. Brown the roulades on all sides. Add the diced carrots, bouillon cube and tomatoes.   ◆ Add the wine, cover and reduce heat. Cook covered, on very low heat, for 1 to 1 1/4 hours, turning several times during cooking. (If sauce evaporates completely, add a little more wine and lower heat further.)
Serves 4-6.

Low in: **cal carb chol**

Jamaican Sour Steak

The combination of red meat and vinegar is exotic & wonderful. What's more, in addition to the special flavor, the vinegar cuts the heavy quality of the beef. Try this Jamaican dish for a new taste treat. Simple to make.

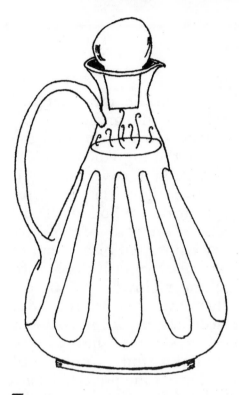

2 lbs. **Swiss Steak**
cut in 4 one-half inch slices
2 T. **Corn Oil**
1/2 c. **Wine Vinegar**
1/4 t. **Salt**
generous grating **Black Pepper**
5-6 cloves, smashed, **Garlic**

*Bird
& Beast
51*

In a frying pan, sauté the steak slices in the oil, until lightly browned on both sides.
◆ **R**emove the meat to a baking dish. Cover with the smashed garlic, salt and pepper. Pour the vinegar over it, cover, and bake in a very slow oven—about 250°—for about 1 1/2 hours.

Serves 4-6.

Low in: **cal carb chol**

Hickory-Smoked Chuck Roast

An inexpensive cut of meat, trimmed of fat, and marinated; then roasted over hickory chips on a barbecue, turns into an elegant and flavorful main dish. Without an outdoor grill this is simply not worth making.

Chuck Pot Roast, *2 lbs.*
  about 1 1/4" thick
Garlic, *5 cloves, cut into slivers*
Corn Oil, *2 T.*
Wine Vinegar, *1/4 c.*
Worcestershire Sauce, *1 T.*
Basil, *1 t. dry*
Black Pepper, *freshly ground*
Tabasco, *3-4 drops*
Hickory Chips *for the barbecue*

Bird
& Beast
52

Cut gashes in the meat and stud meat with garlic slivers.
♦ **M**ake a marinade with the rest of the ingredients. Place the meat in it, cover, and let it sit overnight in the refrigerator.   ♦ **F**ollow the directions on your bag of hickory chips, and place them in your charcoal grill along with the near-glowing charcoal. When the charcoal is ready, place meat on grill and cover it with a sheet of heavy duty aluminum foil. Cook until you have your preferred state of done-ness. Then turn the meat over to the other side, cover again with foil, and cook until done.

Serves 4-6.

Low in: **cal carb chol**

Zwiebel-rostbraten

This hearty beef dish depends upon your ability to peel & slice 4 large onions without shedding tears into the frying pan. An inexpensive cut of meat, smothered in onions, is transformed into a succulent feast — but strictly for onion lovers.

Heat the oil in a large fying pan. Add the onions, stir, and cover the pan. Cook, stirring occasionally, for about 10 minutes. ◆ **U**ncover the pan and lay the slices of meat on the onions. Use some of the onions to cover the top of the meat as well. ◆ **B**reak up the bouillon cube and add to the pan, along with a liberal grinding of black pepper. Cover the pan, turn the heat down, and simmer for 45 minutes, turning the meat over at least once during the cooking. ◆ **U**ncover the pan. You will see that some water has accumulated from the onions. This needs to be boiled off and you do so by raising the heat and keeping the lid off. When liquid is down, drain off fat residue and serve meat smothered in the sautéed onions.

Serves 4-6.

Low in: **cal carb chol**

2-3 slices of **Cross Rib**
trimmed carefully of fat
4 large sliced thin, **Onions**
1 **Beef Bouillon Cube**
1 t. freshly ground **Black Pepper**
2 T. **Corn Oil**

Bird & Beast

53

Middle Eastern Stew

The cumin and cinnamon seasonings add a different and delightfully new flavor to a zesty combination of meat and fresh vegetables —a "one-pot" meal, marvelously simple to prepare.

Ground Beef, 1 1/2 lbs. lean
Onion, 1 chopped
Garlic, 2 cloves, smashed
Carrots, 3
   scraped and cut into 1" chunks
Potato, 1
   peeled and cut into large dice
Cabbage, 1 small head, quartered
Salt, 1/2 t.
Cumin, 1 t. ground
Cinnamon, 1/2 t.
Marjoram, 1/2 t.
Pepper, 1/2 t. freshly ground
Corn Oil, 2 T.

Bird
& Beast
54

Sauté the onion and garlic in the corn oil, in a large stew pot, until the onion is soft and golden.   ◆**A**dd the ground beef and stir, until the meat loses its red color.   ◆**N**ow add the spices, and stir them totally into the meat-onion mixture.   ◆**N**ext, add the carrots and the potato, and mix these vegetables into the meat mixture. Cover the pot, lower the heat, and simmer for 30 minutes, stirring occasionally.   ◆**T**he cabbage is added at this stage because it requires less cooking time than the potatoes and carrots. Add the cabbage, cover and continue cooking until the cabbage is tender. This will take about 15 minutes more. Stir all the ingredients so that the vegetables and meat are thoroughly mixed together. Correct the seasoning, and serve hot.

Serves 4-6.

Low in: **cal carb chol**

Tomato Beef

A simple union of meat and vegetables, Chinese style, with all the no-no's eliminated, & with an emphasis on tomato.

Make a marinade of the garlic, ginger, soya sauce, 1 T. oil, pepper and sherry. Marinate the meat in this for at least 1/2 hour, stirring it around several times. This is more authentically done with a chopstick, of course. ◆ **H**eat up a large frying pan (or wok) and add the rest of the oil. Keep on a moderate heat and add the following ingredients, in the order specified: (a) delayered onion: stir-fry for 1 minute (b) celery: stir-fry for 1 minute more (c) tomatoes: stir-fry for 20 seconds more (d) pineapple chunks: stir-fry for 10 seconds more. ◆ **N**ow add the meat *and* the marinade. Stir-fry for about 1 to 2 minutes more. The vegetables should be crisp and the meat should have lost its red color. Do not overcook and serve immediately.

Serves 3-4.

Low in: **cal carb chol**

1 lb., *sliced thin,* **Beef***
2 cloves chopped **Garlic**
2 slices fresh chopped **Ginger**
1 t. **Soya Sauce**
3 T. **Corn Oil**
freshly ground, to taste, **Pepper**
2 T. **Dry Sherry**
1 large **Onion**
cut in quarters, and de-layered
3 stalks **Celery**
cut on the diagonal, 1 1/2" pieces
1 can **Water Chestnuts**
drained and cut into slices
1 small can **Pineapple Chunks**
(water-packed, no sugar added), drained
3 large, quartered **Tomatoes**

Bird
& Beast
55

---

*Use sirloin steak, flank steak or chuck steak. Paper-thin slices, completely trimmed of fat, are the key.

Ginger Beef

Out goes the corn starch, MSG and sugar from this traditional ginger beef recipe—reducing calories and chemical additives in one blow! The good flavor of all the other ingredients is actually enhanced by such an omission.

Sirloin Steak, *1 lb.*
cut in thin strips, all fat trimmed
Onion, *1 large, cut in slices*
Garlic, *1 large clove, chopped*
Ginger, *1 T. fresh,* sliced*
Corn Oil, *2 T.*
Soya Sauce, *1 T.*
Lemon Juice, *1 T.*
Almonds, *1/4 c. unblanched*
toasted and chopped

Bird
& Beast
56

Combine the soya sauce and the lemon juice and set aside.
◆ **H**eat 2 T. oil, in a large frying pan or wok, until the oil is very hot. (This is a quick stir-fry recipe, and it is necessary to do this on high heat throughout.) ◆ **F**ry the onions quickly—about 15 seconds, shaking pan to keep them from sticking. Add the garlic and ginger, and fry for about 15 seconds more. ◆ **A**dd the beef and stif-fry for about 1 minute more. Add the liquid mixture, and stir-fry for another 30 seconds. ◆ **P**lace the meat-onion mixture onto a heated platter and sprinkle the freshly toasted, chopped almonds on top. This recipe is best when served immediately.

Serves 3-4.

*You can use 2 t. ground ginger in an emergency, but once you have used the fresh, you won't be satisfied with ground ginger for this dish.

Low in: **cal carb chol**

Steak Fit for a King

This has to be the most wonderful sauce for a steak ever. Use it to marinate the steak in —then serve it warmed, over the cooked meat. This is a guaranteed winner on all counts of eating and waist-watching.

Combine all sauce ingredients in a saucepan. Bring to a boil. Reduce heat and simmer for 15 to 20 minutes. Cool completely.   ◆ **P**lace meat in a shallow dish and cover with sauce. Marinate for 2 to 4 hours.   ◆ **R**emove meat and broil, or charcoal grill. Cut meat into slices and pour warm sauce over the slices. Serve immediately.

Serves 5-6.

Low in: **cal carb chol**

2-3 lb. piece of **London Broil** or **Flank Steak**

SAUCE:

12 filets, mashed, **Anchovy**
1 1/4 c. **Red Wine**
1/2 c. **Brandy**
3/4 c. fresh sliced **Mushrooms**
1 can **Tomato Paste**
1/4 c. **Corn Oil**
1/2 c. finely chopped **Parsley**
6 cloves, smashed, **Garlic**
to taste, **Pepper**

Bird & Beast
57

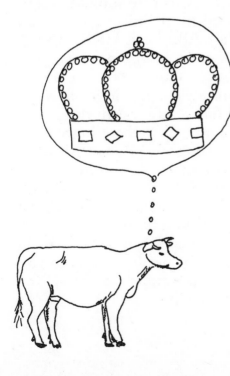

Beef & Shining Noodles

A good Chinese grocery will offer lots of exotic food delights, including "shining noodles" — sometimes called bean threads. These are made from mung beans and are considerably less in caloric value than the more familiar wheat noodles.

Chinese Mushrooms, *4 dried*
Onion, *1 large, sliced thin*
Garlic, *1 large clove, in slivers*
Green Pepper, *1, sliced thin*
Mushrooms, *1/4 lb. fresh sliced*
Black Pepper, *freshly ground, to taste*
Beef Bouillon *Cube, 1*
Mustard Powder, *1 t.*
Soya Sauce, *1 T.*
Water Chestnuts, *1 small can drained and sliced*
Bamboo Shoots, *1 small can drained and sliced*
Bean Threads, *1 small package*
Corn Oil, *2 T.*
Flank Steak, *1 lb.*

Bird & Beast
58

Serves 4-5.

Low in: **cal chol**

Do these preparations first: **a.** Soak dried mushrooms in hot water for 30 minutes. When soft, drain & slice. Reserve liquid. **b.** Soak bean threads in warm water for 15 minutes. Drain. **c.** Slice meat in small, thin strips. ◆ **H**eat oil in a large skillet or wok & add onion & garlic. Cook for about 5 minutes, until onion just begins to soften. Add green pepper & stir-fry for about 5 minutes more.
◆ **A**dd meat & seasonings and stir-fry for 5 minutes—only until meat loses its red coloring. Add both kinds of mushrooms, bouillon cube & soya sauce. Cover & cook for 10 minutes, on low heat.
◆ **L**ast, add bean threads & blend all the ingredients thoroughly. Reduce heat & simmer for 5 minutes, uncovered. You may need to add more liquid at this stage, & the water you have reserved from the mushroom soak may be added if needed. Taste to correct seasoning, & serve immediately.

Veal Marsala à la Wharfhouse

At the Wharfhouse Restaurant on Cortes Island, B. C., owner-chef P. Snow created this scrumptious veal dish, which is a hit with summer diners. She has generously shared her recipe for adaptation here.

Veal Scallops, *1 lb.*
  cut into 2" pieces
Corn Oil Margarine, *2 T.*
Corn Oil, *2 T.*
Mushrooms, *1/2 lb., quartered*
Onion Soup Mix, *1 T.*
Worcestershire Sauce, *1 t.*
Tamari Soya Sauce, *1 t.*
Marsala, *1/2 c.*
Grated Parmesan Cheese, *1/2 c.*

Bird
& Beast
60

Roll the pieces of veal in the grated cheese. ◆ **In** a large, heavy skillet, sauté the veal, a few pieces at a time, until browned on both sides. Do not crowd the veal in the skillet. Remove veal to a heated platter. ◆ **In** the same pan, now sauté the mushrooms until browned lightly. Remove them to the veal platter.

◆ **To** the juices in the pan, add the onion soup mix, the Worcestershire sauce, the tamari and the Marsala. With a spatula, scrape the bits of meat and cheese from bottom of pan and blend thoroughly.

◆ **R**aise the heat and simmer sauce for 1 to 2 minutes. Return the veal and the mushrooms to pan and turn the meat gently in the sauce, so that meat and sauce are well blended. Serve immediately.

Serves 3-4.

Low in: **cal carb chol**

Mustard Lamb

Lamb is not usually seen on a diet. Yet, with fat carefully trimmed off, a boneless leg, done in a simple mustard and sherry coating, may add variety and interest to your dining experience, without excessive breach of our diet principles.

Make a paste of the mustard and sherry. With a pastry brush, paint the paste thickly all over the surface of the lamb. ◆ **P**re-heat oven to 350° and place the lamb on a rack in a roasting pan. This will allow most of the remaining lamb fat to drain off during the roasting. Roast the leg for 1 to 1 1/2 hours, until done. (Lamb does not need to be well done, unless you actually prefer it that way. It is quite delicious when it is a little pink at the center.) ◆ **S**lice thin and serve warm, with more Dijon mustard as a garnish.

1 boneless **Leg of Lamb**
carefully trimmed of fat
1/2 c. **Dijon Mustard***
1/4 c. **Dry Sherry**

Bird & Beast
59

Serves 6-10.

Use any good mustard instead of Dijon, if you prefer —but never, never use hot-dog mustard for this dish.

Low in: **cal carb**

Veal with Lemon

The quality of this dish depends largely upon the quality of the veal you bring home from the butcher shop. If you can't get true white veal, then skip this recipe and find something else to make for dinner.

Dip each piece of veal into the grated cheese, so that each side has a light coating. ◆ **In** a large, heavy skillet, heat the oil and margarine, so that they are quite hot. Add the veal, *in one layer.* (You may have to do this in several turns, but if you try to crowd all the meat together into the pan, the liquid will turn watery and the dish will be ruined. *So don't do it.*) ◆ **C**ook the veal over relatively high heat until brown. Turn, and brown the other side. This should take only a few moments. (If you are doing this in turns, remove one lot to a heated platter while you are browning the next group.) ◆ **R**emove meat, pour off all remaining fat from pan and add the vermouth. With a spatula, work particles of meat and cheese from the pan into the wine. Bring wine to a simmer and add the lemon juice. Return all meat to pan, and turn the meat carefully through the hot lemon-wine sauce. Season to taste with freshly ground black pepper. ◆ **T**ransfer the meat to a heated platter and garnish with lemon slices and fresh parsley.

Serves 3-4.

1 lb. **Veal Scallops**
cut into 2" pieces
1/4 c. **Grated Parmesan Cheese**
2 T. **Corn Oil Margarine**
2 T. **Corn Oil**
3 T. fresh **Lemon Juice**
6 thin slices of **Lemon**
1/4 c. **Dry White Vermouth**

Bird & Beast

61

Low in: **cal carb chol**

Veal in Yogurt

This is one of my favorite all-time recipes. Originally, it was made with sour cream. Now I use yogurt, which makes a perfectly wonderful sauce for the delicate veal. The slightly spicy flavor gives the dish a special quality. A dandy company-for-dinner entrée.

Veal Scallops, *1 lb.*
  cut in 2" pieces
Corn Oil Margarine, *2 T.*
Corn Oil, *2 T.*
Onions, *2 medium, sliced thin*
Garlic, *2 cloves, minced*
Beef Bouillon Cubes, *2*
Mustard Powder, *1 T.*
Paprika, *3 t.*
Parsley, *3 T. fresh, minced*
Yogurt, *1 c.*
Mushrooms, *1/2 lb. fresh, sliced*

In a large skillet, sauté the mushrooms in the margarine until they are deeply browned. Remove the mushrooms and set aside.   ◆**A**dd the oil to the skillet and sauté the onions and garlic until soft. Dry the veal thoroughly and add it to the onions in the pan. Sauté for a few minutes more, until veal loses its pink color. This should take about 5 minutes.
◆**A**dd the bouillon cubes, mustard, paprika and parsley, and blend thoroughly. Reduce heat, cover, and simmer for 30 minutes.   ◆**U**ncover, add mushrooms and yogurt. Heat through, but do not boil. Serve immediately.

Serves 3-4.

Low in: **cal carb chol**

Stuffed Vine Leaves

This recipe is something of a production, because of the wash-rinse-wash-rinse process of debrining the vine leaves. But if you've got the time to give it a try, you'll be delightfully rewarded in the eating.

If your vine leaves have been preserved in a jar or barrel, soak them first in a large bowl in very hot water for 10 minutes. Make sure the leaves are separated from each other during the soaking time & that the water penetrates each. Drain & rinse thoroughly with cold water. Drain again. Now *repeat* the entire process. This removes the excess salt from the leaves & is a critical step.

♦ **I**n a large bowl, mix meat, onions, tomato, smashed garlic, aromatics & seasonings, until all are well blended.

♦ **P**lace one leaf on a plate & put a tablespoon of filling in center. Fold top down, then sides, and roll up, like a cigar. Fill all the leaves this way.

♦ **P**lace a layer of 5-6 unfilled vine leaves in bottom of large frying pan. (This prevents the rolled vine leaves from sticking.) Place stuffed leaves tightly together in one layer in the pan. Place garlic slivers between rolled leaves. Sprinkle with lemon juice & add 1/2 cup water. Cover pan & simmer

1/2 lb. preserved, drained **Vine Leaves**
2 lbs. lean **Ground Beef**
1 1/2 minced **Onions**
1 large minced **Tomato**
3 cloves, smashed, **Garlic**
3 more cloves, slivered, **Garlic**
3 T. chopped fresh **Parsley**
1 T. dried **Mint Leaves**
1 t. **Cinnamon**
1/2 t. **Allspice**
to taste, **Pepper**
juice of one **Lemon**
1/2 c. **Water**

Bird & Beast

63

---

over gentle heat for 2 hours. Check from time to time to see if more water is needed. May be served hot or warm.

Serves 6-8.

Low in: **cal carb chol**

Mitzutaki

The ingredients for this Japanese Hot Pot can be varied, to individual taste as well as to specific diet considerations. It is a wonderfully easy and most impressive company dinner, but is difficult to do without an electric frying pan.

Sirloin Steak, *1 to 1 1/2 lbs.*
  very thinly sliced
Chicken Breasts, *1 to 1 1/2 lbs.*
  boned and cut into 1" pieces
Celery Cabbage, *2 c.*
  cut in 1" strips
Mushrooms, *1/2 lb., sliced thickly*
Green Onions, 1 bunch
  cut in 2" lengths
Chicken Broth,* *1 1/2 quarts*
Tofu, *2 cakes*
  drained and cut into 1" cubes
Watercress, *cut in 2" lengths*
Cod, Oysters or **Shrimp,** *1 lb.*
  (or any combination of these)

THE SAUCE:

Lemon Juice, *1/2 c.*
Kikko Soya Sauce, *1/2 c.*
Chicken Broth, *1/2 c.*
Cayenne Pepper, *pinch*
Daikon,** *1 c. grated*

Bird
& Beast
64

You may use canned stock, home-made stock or stock from good quality chicken bouillon cubes.

**Daikon is a white radish, found in oriental food shops.*

On a very large platter, arrange the meat, fish, and vegetables attractively. (Or, you may want to divide these and place them on three separate dishes.) ◆ **M**ake the sauce by combining all sauce ingredients. Distribute the sauce in small dishes, one for each diner. ◆ **I**n an electric frying pan, heat the broth until boiling. Place the pan in the center of the dining room table and keep the broth at a simmer. ◆ **E**ach diner is now on his/her own. Using chopsticks (no cheating!), each person places into the broth the morsels she/he has chosen and cooks them until done to taste. Then the morsels are removed, and dipped in the sauce to cool and eat. ◆ **W**hen all meat and vegetables have been cooked and eaten, divide the soup, which has become very rich and flavorful, and which then tops off the meal.

Low in: **cal carb chol**

FISH ENTRÉES

Flounder Sicilian Style

Il Faro in New York City used to serve this marvelous fish dish and I would order it every time I ate there, bypassing their other excellent fare. I have experimented with the recipe and produced what I think is a really close approximation, geared to the diet-conscious.

With 1 T. oil, brush the underside of each fish lightly. Slash both sides with 3 diagonal cuts, and place under a very hot broiler, about 2″ from broiling element. Broil for about 7 to 10 minutes on each side—depending on the thickness of the fish. (Fish filets will take considerably less time.) Do not overcook.
◆ **W**hile fish is broiling, make a paste of the rest of the oil, salt, pepper, breadcrumbs, garlic, parsley, herbs, and cheese. ◆ **R**emove the fish from the oven and spread the paste over the top side of the fish only. Return to the broiler and broil for 3 to 5 minutes more—or until the topping is crusty. ◆ **W**hen done, place on a heated platter, sprinkle with wine vinegar and serve hot.

Serves 2-4.

Flounder or sole filets may be substituted for the whole fish. However, it is much more in character to use the whole fish for this dish.

2 whole, cleaned & dressed, **Flounder***
3 T. **Corn Oil**
1/4 t. **Salt**
freshly ground, to taste, **Pepper**
1/4 c. **Breadcrumbs**
3 large cloves, chopped fine, **Garlic**
2 T. chopped **Parsley**
2 T. **Grated Parmesan Cheese**
1 T. **Red Wine Vinegar**
1/2 t. **Oregano**
1/2 t. **Dried Basil**

Fish

◆

67

Low in: **cal carb chol**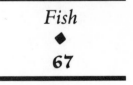

Halibut Cilantro

While this may be the simplest fish recipe ever, the eating rewards are nontheless substantial. Highly recommended for salt-free dieters and calorie/carbohydrate counters.

Halibut, *2 1/2" slices*
Cilantro, ** *1 bunch, chopped*
  (use leaves and stems)
Corn Oil Margarine, *2 T.*
Black Pepper, *freshly ground*
Lemon Juice, *1-2 T. fresh-squeezed*

Fish

◆

68

Begin by washing, drying and chopping the cilantro.
◆ **B**roil the fish about 5 minutes on each side. Be sure not to overcook, though; otherwise fish will be dry and tasteless. ◆ **M**elt the margarine and add the lemon juice (more, if you like the flavor very lemony). Do this while the fish is broiling. ◆ **R**emove fish to a heated platter. Pour sauce over slices and add ground pepper. Sprinkle chopped cilantro liberally over top and serve.

Serves 2-3.

*Any other thick sliced white fish may be used in place of halibut with equally good results. But fish for this dish should be fresh and not frozen.

**See note at bottom of page 18.

Low in: **cal carb chol**

Salmon Quiche Sue

This light and economical salmon quiche lost its crust and most of its calories —but none of its flavor.

Prepare a 9″ pie plate by greasing it lightly with one tablespoon of the corn oil margarine. ◆ **C**ook onion in the rest of the margarine for several minutes, until soft. Blend in flour, salt and pepper. ◆ **I**n a mixing bowl, mix together the liquid from the can, the evaporated milk, eggs, and cheese. Mash salmon and combine with liquid-cheese mixture. Add peas and dillweed. ◆ **P**our this mixture into the prepared pie plate and bake in a preheated 375° oven for 35 to 45 minutes, or until set. Allow to cool slighly before cutting into it, otherwise cheese will still be too runny to allow for slices.

Serves 4-6.

Low in: **cal carb**

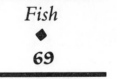

1 medium, minced, **Onion**
3 T. **Corn Oil Margarine**
2 T. **Flour**
1 t. **Salt**
1/2 t. freshly ground **Pepper**
3/4 c. **Evaporated Milk**
1 can (7 3/4 oz.) **Salmon**
plus liquid
2 slightly beaten **Eggs**
1 T. **Dillweed**
1 small can, drained, **Peas**
1 c. **Grated Cheddar Cheese**

Fish

◆

69

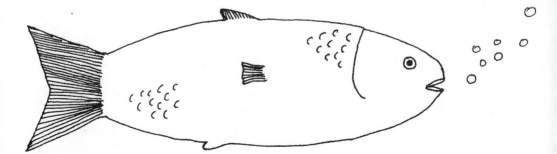

Kippered Salmon Salad

Almost like a salmon mousse and incredibly easy to prepare, this recipe depends wholly on your ability to purchase a piece of "kippered" salmon that is both smoked and cooked. Many local fish stores carry this salmon delicacy, which is NOT the same as lox.

"Kippered" Salmon, *3/4 lb. piece*
Eggs, *4 hard-boiled*
Onion, *1 large*
Mayonnaise, *1/2 c. best quality*

Fish
◆
70

Trim the skin from the salmon and chop it until it disintegrates into a paste. (A food processor will do this for you in a few seconds.) ◆**W**ith a large fork, mash the eggs and blend with the salmon paste.
◆**M**ince the onions very fine and add this to the salmon.
◆**L**ast, add the mayonnaise and stir to blend all ingredients. This is delectable as an appetizer, or as a fish entrée.

Serves 4-6.

Low in: **cal carb**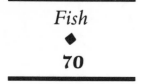

Cioppino (for a crowd)

Almost every fish enthusiast has his or her own version of cioppino.* I generally make use of the best, cheapest and freshest fish in the market that day to produce a low-calorie, low-carbohydrate, low-fat epicurean feast. This recipe should feed ten hungry adults.

2 large, fresh cracked **Crabs***
1 lb. raw, in shell, **Shrimp***
2 lbs. fresh, in shell, **Clams***
washed thoroughly
2 lbs., cut in pieces, **Fish***
2 medium **Onions**
3 large cloves, chopped, **Garlic**
2 T., chopped, **Parsley**
2 stalks, chopped fine, **Celery**
1/2, chopped fine, **Green Pepper**
1/4 c. **Corn Oil**
1 28-oz. can **Italian Plum Tomatoes**
(with juice)
1 can **Tomato Sauce**
1 can **Tomato Paste**
1/2 t. **Salt**
1 T. dried **Basil**
1 t. dried **Oregano**
freshly ground, to taste, **Pepper**
3/4 bottle **Dry Red Wine**
about 2 cups **Water**

Make the sauce first by sautéing the onions, garlic, celery, parsley and pepper in oil, until the vegetables are soft.
◆ **A**dd the tomatoes, tomato sauce, tomato paste, seasonings, and dried herbs and blend with the vegetables.
◆ **A**dd the wine and simmer the sauce for 15 to 20 minutes over low heat. ◆ **A**dd the water and bring to a boil.
◆ **N**ow, add the fish in stages, beginning with the varieties which need the longest cooking time: **a.** Add raw fish and cook for 10 minutes. **b.** Add crabs, shrimp and clams, and cook for 10 minutes more, adding more water if necessary. Do not overcook fish. **c.** Taste to correct seasoning.
◆ **S**erve in individual soup bowls, with a good ladling of fish & broth in each serving.

Low in: **cal carb chol**

Fish
◆
71

*Fish ingredients may vary —depending on what's available and on your own taste and pocketbook. Cioppino — "chipping in"—came from fishermen contributing their left-overs from the day's catch to the Fisherman's Wharf communal pot. Rock cod, sea bass, halibut, ling cod, snapper, etc. are all good candidates.

Crab Piquant

With crab costing as much as diamonds, you might want to use a crab substitute for this dish. On the other hand, for a splurge, you may wish to give yourself the pleasure of fresh cracked crab meat.

Spinach, *2 large bunches, fresh (or 2 packages frozen)*
Onion, *1 large, minced*
Corn Oil Margarine, *3 T.*
Crab Meat, *1 lb. (fresh or canned)*
Dry Sherry, *1/4 c.*
Yogurt, *2/3 c.*
Nutmeg, *1 t.*
Garlic, *1 large clove, smashed*
Pepper, to taste
Salt, *1/4 t.*
Grated Mozzarella, *1/2 c. or other low-fat cheese*

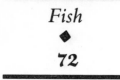

Fish
◆
72

Cook, drain and chop the spinach. Spread the spinach in one layer on the bottom of a 2-quart casserole dish which has been greased with 1 T. corn oil margarine.   ◆**S**auté the onion in the other 2 T. margarine until brown. Then add the crab meat and just *heat* through. (Do not cook.) ◆**R**emove from heat. Add sherry, yogurt, nutmeg, garlic, salt and pepper. Blend all together and place this mixture on top of spinach. ◆**S**prinkle grated cheese all over top. Bake at 350° for 40 minutes or until bubbly.

Serves 4-6.

Low in: **cal carb**

Lemon Sauté Shrimp

This excellent and easy-to-prepare dish uses garlic and lemon in abundance to bring out the best taste of fresh shrimp.

Clean the shrimp, rinse them, and pat them thoroughly dry. ◆ Heat the oil in a large skillet and sauté the shrimp and garlic together until shrimp turn pink. This takes about 5 minutes. ◆ Add the lemon juice, salt, pepper and chopped parsley. Stir to blend, over high heat, for about 30 seconds. Remove and serve hot, with a tossed green salad.

Serves 3-4.

Low in: **cal carb**

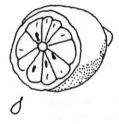

1 lb. fresh, in their shells, **Shrimp**
4 large cloves, cut in slivers, **Garlic**
juice of 2 **Lemons**
1/4 t. **Salt**
freshly ground, to taste, **Pepper**
1/2 c. fresh, chopped **Parsley**
2 T. **Corn Oil**

Fish

◆

73

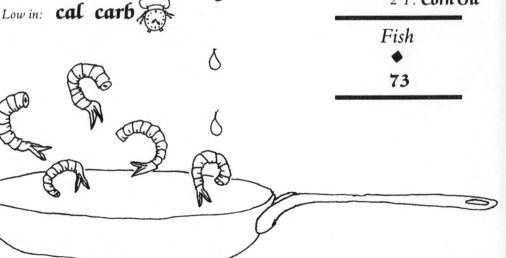

Cod Provençale

There is nothing so wonderfully aromatic as this simple provençale sauce to adorn filet of cod (or any other thick white fish in season).

Cod, *4 6-oz. fresh filets rinsed and patted dry*
Dry White Wine, *1 c.*
Stewed Tomatoes, *1 14-oz. can*
Corn Oil, *2 T.*
Green Pepper, *1 large, chopped*
Chili Pepper, *1 small, chopped*
Onion, *1 medium size, chopped*
Garlic, *1 large clove, chopped*
Thyme, *1/2 t. ground*
Bay Leaf, *1*
Salt, *1/4 t.*
Pepper, *freshly ground, to taste*
Grated Mozzarella Cheese, *1/2 c. (optional)*

Fish

◆

74

Poach the cod in the wine, in a covered sauté pan, for about 10 minutes. ◆ **I**n a large frying pan, heat the oil and sauté the onion, garlic and both kinds of pepper for about 5 minutes, stirring frequently. Add the tomatoes, thyme, bay leaf, salt and ground pepper. Blend all ingredients, lower heat, and simmer for about 10 minutes, stirring occasionally. ◆ **R**emove fish to a heated platter and douse with the sauce. Grated cheese may be sprinkled on top if you like; but even without the cheese, this fish dish can still win friends.

Serves 3-4.

Low in: **cal carb chol**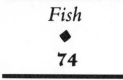

Poached Salmon with Grapefruit Stuffing

Brigitte Vogt introduced me to the simple but elegant union of salmon and grapefruit. If you can afford the price of a whole salmon these days and want to impress the multitudes, this version is a knockout —with almost no effort to it.

Line a roasting pan with a large piece of heavy-duty aluminum foil, allowing for enough extra foil to wrap around the fish. Place fish into pan. Baste inside and out with melted margarine. ◆ **P**lace the slices of one grapefruit in the fish cavity. ◆ **P**our vermouth into the pan and season fish with freshly ground pepper. Make a canopy with the foil and seal the fish in completely. ◆ **P**lace pan in a pre-heated 350° oven to poach for 30 to 40 minutes. Do not overcook. ◆ **W**hen done, remove grapefruit and place whole salmon on a serving platter. Garnish with slices of the other grapefruit, and serve immediately.

Serves 6-8.

*Centre bone removed is ever so much nicer, but not by any means essential.

1 whole, ca. 4-5 lbs., **Salmon**
cleaned & dressed*
2 sliced **Grapefruits**
(do not remove skins)
Corn Oil Margarine
2 T., melted
to taste, **Pepper**
1 c. **Dry White Vermouth**

Fish
◆
75

---

cal carb chol

Copalis Beach Chowder Nina Rose

This is another recipe where the ingredients may vary with either the season or with the dieter's individual preferences. If I'm feeling thin, I'll add 1-2 potatoes; if I'm feeling fat, I'll leave them out. This dish seems to please either way.

Cod, *2 1/2 lbs.*
  cut up into 2" pieces
Shrimp Meat, *1/2 lb.*
Potatoes, *1-2 small*
  peeled and cut up
Onions, *2, minced*
Carrots, *2-3, peeled and sliced*
Corn Oil, *2 T.*
Summer Savory, *1 T.*
Dillweed, *1 t.*
Salt, *1/4 t.*
Pepper, *to taste*
Yogurt, *2/3 c.*
Milk, *2/3 c.*
Frozen Green Beans
  1 pkg. (cut style)

Fish

◆

76

Put potatoes and carrots in a saucepan. Cover with water and cook until vegetables are tender.   ◆ In a large frying pan, sauté the onions until brown. Add the cod and brown the fish quickly, over medium heat.   ◆ Lower heat, and add the savory, dillweed, salt, pepper and garlic. Add shrimp. Mix together until all ingredients are blended.   ◆ Add the milk and with a wooden spoon or spatula, scrape all pieces of fish and onion up from bottom of pan. Add the yogurt and carrots and potatoes. Warm through.   ◆ Taste to correct seasoning and serve hot.

Serves 6-8.

Low in: **cal carb chol**

Snapper Alejandro

Definitely for garlic lovers — a dish that will respect your waistline but will play havoc with your social relationships.

Rinse the fish and pat it dry. Cut it into 4 pieces. ◆ **H**eat the oil in a large frying pan. Add the fish and seasonings and brown on both sides. Remove to a heated platter. ◆ **A**dd the minced garlic to the pan and sauté until browned, stirring frequently. Spread the garlic all over the tops of each piece of snapper and serve immediately. ◆ **G**arnish with chopped cilantro if you wish.

Serves 4-6.

Low in: **cal carb chol**

2 lbs. filets, **Red Snapper**
3 T. **Corn Oil**
8-10 large cloves, minced, **Garlic**
1/4 t. **Salt**
to taste, **Pepper**
(optional) **Cilantro**

Fish

◆

77

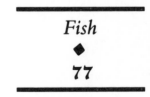

Shrimp & Vegetables for a Summer Tuesday Luncheon

We have Harry Locke to thank once again for this simple but simply exquisite stir-fry shrimp & vegetable dish —not recommended for cholesterol-restricted diets. But if you are a shrimp eater, you will find this medley a winner.

Corn Oil, *2 T.*
Salt, *1/4 t.*
Carrots, *2*
  scraped & cut in chunks, on the diagonal
Celery, *2 stalks*
  cut in chunks, on the diagonal
Onions, *2 medium, delayered*
  (as in the Tomato-Beef recipe)
Water Chestnuts, *1 can*
  drained and sliced
Baby Corn, *1 small can, drained*
Straw Mushrooms, *1 can*
  drained and halved
Shrimp, *1 lb.*
Garlic Powder, *1 t.*
Pepper, *freshly ground, to taste*
Bok Choy, *3 c.*
Soya Sauce, *1 T.*

Fish

◆

78

Wash and clean the shrimp. Pat them thoroughly dry. ◆**B**lanch the carrots and the celery by dipping them in boiling water; about 2 minutes for the celery, about 4 minutes for the carrots. Drain. ◆**W**ash and trim the bok choy. Drain, and cut into 2″ pieces on the diagonal. ◆**H**eat the oil in a large skillet or wok until very hot. Add salt. ◆**A**dd the blanched celery and carrots and stir-fry for 2 minutes. ◆**A**dd the water chestnuts, baby corn and straw mushrooms. Stir-fry for 1 minute. ◆**A**dd the shrimp, garlic powder and pepper. Stir-fry for 1 minute more. ◆**N**ow, add bok choy. Stir-fry for another minute. ◆**R**emove from heat and toss all ingredients with 1 T. soya sauce. Taste to correct seasoning.

Serves 4-6.

Low in: **cal carb**

EGGS 'N' THINGS

Vegetarian Entrées

Cottage Cheese Soufflé

Try this simple-to-prepare, light and delicious variation of the standard cheese soufflé. Substitute cottage cheese, well drained, for the higher-fat cheese, to reduce both cholesterol and calorie intake —and find both pleasure and virtuousness!

Corn Oil Margarine, *2 T.*
Onion, *1 small, minced*
Flour, *1 T.*
Salt, *1/8 t.*
Milk, *1 c.*
Cottage Cheese,* *1 c. small curd well-drained*
Eggs, *4, separated*
Cayenne, *1/2 t.*

In a saucepan, heat the margarine and sauté the onion until well browned. Blend in flour, salt and cayenne. Gradually stir in milk and cook over medium heat, stirring constantly until mixture thickens. ◆ **R**emove from heat and stir in cheese. ◆ **I**n a small bowl, beat the egg yolks and stir these gradually into the cheese mixture. ◆ **B**eat the egg whites, preferably with an electric mixer, until they are quite stiff. ◆ **F**old the cheese mixture into the eggwhite—about half at a time—taking care not to break down the stiff consistency of the whites. ◆ **P**our into a 1 1/2 quart soufflé dish that has been lightly greased with corn oil margarine and bake in a preheated 350° oven until puffed and brown. Serve immediately.

Serves 4-5.

Start draining the cottage cheese about 30 minutes before you begin this recipe, since you want to give it lots of time to shed its liquid.

Low in: **cal carb**

Ricotta Pie

Stanley Feder gave me the original recipe from his own kitchen; I adapted it to my taste. This easy-to-make cheese pie can be served warm or cold, as an elegant hors d'oeuvre, a luncheon entrée, or a Saturday night supper, with a tossed green salad.

Preheat oven to 350°.
◆ **M**ix together the ricotta, the eggs, the flour, the Parmesan, the onion flakes, the salt and pepper, and one teaspoon of nutmeg.   ◆ **P**lace the batter into a deep pie dish, which has been greased with corn oil margarine.   ◆ **S**prinkle the rest of the nutmeg all over the top and bake for 30 minutes. Then slip under the broiler for several minutes just to brown the top.

Serves 4-6.

Low in: **cal carb chol***
less than 3/4 egg per 1/6 portion

1 *lb.* **Ricotta Cheese**
4 **Eggs**
6 *T.* **Flour**
1/2 *c.* **Grated Parmesan Cheese**
3 *T.* dehydrated **Onion Flakes**
to taste, **Salt**
to taste, **Pepper**
2 *t.* **Nutmeg**
1 *T.* **Corn Oil Margarine**

Spinach-Ricotta Pie

The combination of spinach and ricotta is familiar to gnocchi lovers. Stanley Feder eliminates the fuss and fury of gnocchi, drastically reduces the flour and produces this superb pie instead. A gnocchi experience for waistwatchers!

Frozen Spinach, *1 10-oz. package*
Ricotta Cheese, *1 lb.*
Eggs, *4*
Grated Parmesan Cheese, *1/2 c.*
Flour, *2 T.*
Nutmeg, *3/4 t. ground*
Black Pepper, *1/4 t. freshly ground*
   (or more to taste)
Salt, *1/8 t.*
Corn Oil Margarine

Preheat oven to 350°.
♦ **C**ook the spinach in a small amount of water until it is heated through. Drain it thoroughly, squeezing out as much water as possible.
♦ **M**ix together the ricotta and eggs. Add the cheese, flour, nutmeg, pepper and salt, mixing thoroughly.
♦ **A**dd the chopped spinach and check the seasoning.
♦ **L**iberally grease a 9″ cake pan with corn oil margarine and spread the ricotta filling evenly in the pan. Bake until the pie has puffed slightly and the center is no longer liquid—about 30 minutes.

Serves 4-6.

Low in: **cal carb chol* o**
*less than 3/4 egg per 1/6 portion

Lucca's Pie

If you are ever in Seattle, don't miss lunch at the Surrogate Hostess, for some of the best healthful food in town. Their Lucca's Pie is my favorite and my mind's tooth led to this duplicate. It's something of a production, so you will want to consider whether you want to make it, or take a trip to Seattle instead.

In a saucepan, sauté the minced onion in the 1 T. oil, until it is soft. Add the defrosted spinach and cook for 3 to 4 minutes.   ◆ **I**n a large bowl beat the eggs. Add the ricotta and the grated Parmesan and blend. Add the spinach-onion mixture and blend all ingredients thoroughly.   ◆ **W**ith the 1 T. corn oil margarine, grease a 9″ pie plate and spread the ricotta-spinach mixture evenly to form the bottom layer.   ◆ **I**n another saucepan, sauté the second onion in the oil until golden, about 5 minutes. Add the garlic and cook for 1 to 2 minutes more. ◆ **A**dd the plum tomatoes and the tomato paste and stir through. Place on a low heat and simmer sauce for 1/2 hour.

◆ **A**dd the 2 cheeses to the sauce, and add pepper to taste. Spread this sauce-cheese layer on top of the ricotta layer. ◆ **B**ake in a preheated 350° oven for 40 minutes. Let set for about 15 minutes before cutting.

BOTTOM LAYER:

1 lb. **Ricotta**
1 10 oz. pkg. **Frozen Spinach**
1 medium **Onion**
1/2 c. **Grated Parmesan Cheese**
2 **Eggs**
1 T. **Corn Oil**

TOP LAYER:

1 T. **Corn Oil**
1 medium **Onion**
2 cloves, chopped, **Garlic**
1 28-oz. can **Plum Tomatoes**
1/2 c. **Grated Gruyere Cheese**
or **Emmenthaler Cheese**
1/2 c. **Grated Parmesan Cheese**
to taste, **Pepper**

1 T. **Corn Oil Margarine**
for greasing pan

Eggs 'n' Things
83

Serves 4-6.

Low in: **cal carb**

Zucchini Pie

This recipe is similar, in its basis, to the zucchini quiches (p. 88-89) but it departs into its own distinctly different variation on that original theme.

Zucchini, *4 c., grated julienne style*
Garlic, *2 cloves, smashed*
Grated Parmesan Cheese, *1 c.*
Grated Emmenthaler, *1 c.*
Bread Crumbs, *1/2 scant c.*
Basil, *1 T. dried*
Salt, *1/2 t.*
Pepper, *freshly ground, to taste*
Eggs, *4, beaten*
Tomatoes, *2, sliced*
Corn Oil Margarine, *1 t.*
Pepperoni Sausage, *sliced (optional)*

Place the grated zucchini in a colander and salt it lightly. Allow it to drain for at least 30 minutes. Press out any excess liquid. ◆ **I**n a mixing bowl, beat the eggs and add the grated, drained zucchini. Add the garlic, bread crumbs, cheeses and seasonings. ◆ **G**enerously spread margarine all over the bottom and sides of a 9″ pie plate, and pour zucchini mixture into it, smoothing it so it is even. Cover top with sliced tomatoes and thin slices of pepperoni sausage, if preferred. ◆ **B**ake in a preheated 375° oven for 30 to 40 minutes, or until nicely browned.

Serves 4-6.

Low in: **cal carb**

Ortega Chili & Cheese Omelet

The combination of ortega green chilis, cheese and eggs makes music in the mouth. Incredibly simple for brunch or light supper fare — for those who enjoy a mild Mexican "bite." Not recommended for cholesterol watchers.

Beat the eggs in a large bowl. Add the chopped chilis and the grated cheese and combine to blend. ◆**I**n a large skillet heat the corn oil margarine until sizzling. Add the egg mixture. ◆**C**ook on medium heat, lifting the sides with a spatula so that the runny egg from the centre goes to the sides for cooking. When all the egg has set, flip half over and continue to cook on a low heat for 2 minutes more. Serve immediately.

Serves 4-6.

Low in: **cal carb**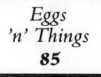

5-6, beaten whole, **Eggs**
Ortega Green Chilis
1/2 can, chopped fine
Monterey Jack Cheese
1/4 lb. grated
1/8 t. **Salt**
freshly ground, to taste, **Pepper**
2 T. **Corn Oil Margarine**

*Eggs
'n' Things*
85

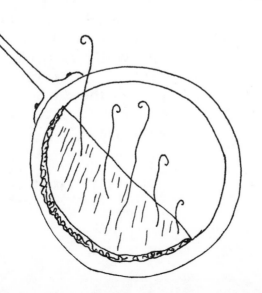

Spinach & Mushroom Omelet

Bill Cliett invented this very simple but elegant light dish for après ski, bulge-battling suppers. That old standby, spinach, harmonizes with sautéed mushrooms and onions to produce a perfect medley.

Onion, *1 small, chopped fine*
Mushrooms, *1/2 can sliced*
  well drained
Corn Oil Margarine, *2 T.*
Frozen Spinach, *1 pkg.*
  thawed but not pre-cooked
Eggs, *5-6*
Salt, *1/8 t.*
Grated Parmesan Cheese, *1/4 c.*

---

*Eggs
'n' Things*
86

Sauté the onion in the margarine, in a large frying pan, until well browned. Add the mushrooms and brown.
◆ **S**pread the thawed spinach on top of the mushroom/onion mixture. ◆ **B**eat the eggs, together with the salt and Parmesan cheese. Pour gently over the spinach mixture. As the egg cooks, lift the edges of the omelet with a spatula so that the liquid egg from centre runs to the sides of the pan to cook. ◆ **R**emove from stove and place the pan under a pre-heated broiler unit to brown the top. ◆ **O**ptions: You may wish to vary this dish with a particular spice or herb. Try 1/2 t. cayenne pepper, for those who like it hot, or 1/2 t. dillweed, for a fresh garden taste.

Serves 4-6.

Low in: **cal carb**

Quiche Niçoise

*If you are a quiche lover,
but are unwilling to indulge your waistline
in the caloric content of the rich crust,
I offer three crustless quiche recipes
as delicious alternatives. Here's the first.*

Pre-heat oven to 375°. ◆ In an 8"-9" frying pan, sauté the onion in 2 T. oil until tender but not brown. ◆ Stir the plum tomatoes into the pan and break them up with a spoon. Add the garlic, herbs and seasonings. Cover pan and cook for 5 minutes over low heat. Uncover, raise heat and cook for 5 minutes or so more — to evaporate the liquid almost entirely. Allow to cool slightly. ◆ Beat the eggs. Add the chopped anchovy filets, the other 2 T. of oil, the tomato paste, the parsley, paprika, cayenne and black pepper and mix until all ingredients are blended. Gradually fold in cooked tomatoes. Check the seasoning. ◆ Liberally grease a 9" quiche pan with the corn oil margarine and spread the quiche filling evenly in the pan. Sprinkle the cheese on the top and bake on the top rack of the oven for 25 to 30 minutes or until puffed and brown on top.

1 medium, chopped, **Onion**
4 T. **Corn Oil**
1 28-oz. can **Italian Plum Tomatoes**
drained and broken up
1 large clove, smashed, **Garlic**
1/2 t. **Oregano**
1/2 t. **Basil**
1/4 t. **Salt**
3 **Eggs**
8 filets, chopped, **Anchovy**
3 T. **Tomato Paste**
3 T. chopped fresh **Parsley**
1 t. **Paprika**
a pinch of **Cayenne Pepper**
a pinch of **Black Pepper**
1/4 c. **Grated Parmesan**
or **Grated Swiss Cheese**
1-2 T. **Corn Oil Margarine**
(for greasing pan)

---

*Eggs
'n' Things*
87

Serves 4-6.

Low in: **cal carb**

Zucchini-Basil Quiche

Discover the wonders of zucchini as a reliable and totally wonderful basis for a cheese tart.

Zucchini, *4 cups, grated julienne style*
Eggs, *4, beaten*
Flour, *1/4 c.*
Basil, *1 t. dried*
Corn Oil Margarine, *2 T.*
Salt, *1/2 t.*
Grated Swiss Cheese, *2/3 c.*
Grated Parmesan Cheese, *2/3 c.*
Pepper, *1/2 t. freshly ground*

Place the grated zucchini in a colander, sprinkle with salt, and allow to stand and drain for *at least* 30 minutes. ◆ **P**ut the drained zucchini into a mixing bowl and add all other ingredients. Mix until well blended. ◆ **G**enerously grease a 9″ pie plate with margarine. Pour the zucchini mixture into this and bake in a preheated 350° oven for 30 to 40 minutes, or until delightfully brown on top.

Serves 4-6.

Low in: **cal carb**

Zucchini-Cheddar Quiche

Many different vegetable-cheese combinations can turn into quiches of the crustless variety. You may wish to experiment with your own version, varying vegetables and cheeses to your own taste, or diet considerations. Zucchini-cheddar is easy-as-pie and equally wonderful.

On the coarse side of the grater, grate the unpeeled, trimmed zucchini. Salt lightly and place in a colander to drain for at least 1/2 hour. ◆ **S**auté the onion in 1 T. margarine, until quite brown. Add zucchini. Cook over high heat, until all moisture has evaporated. Cool. ◆ **B**eat eggs, and add grated cheese. Stir the zucchini mixture into the egg-cheese mixture. Season with pepper.

◆ **T**urn into a 9″ quiche or pie plate which has been greased with the other tablespoon of margarine, spreading the mixture evenly in the dish.

◆ **B**ake in a preheated 350° oven for about 40 to 45 minutes, or until browned and slightly puffed.

Serves 4-6.

Low in: **cal carb**

2 T. **Corn Oil Margarine**
1 large, chopped, **Onion**
2 medium or 3 small, grated, **Zucchini**
5 **Eggs**
3/4 lb. grated **Cheddar Cheese**
or **Monterey Jack Cheese**
1/8 t. **Salt**
freshly ground **Pepper**

*Eggs
'n' Things*
89

Broccoli Timbale

When you are tired of quiche, try a vegetable timbale for a change. Here is the broccoli version — but you might be equally pleased if you should decide to substitute cauliflower or zucchini instead. Timbales are not for cholesterol watchers, as you will see by the numbers of eggs involved.

Broccoli, *1 bunch*
Onion, *1 large, diced fine*
Corn Oil Margarine, *3 T.*
Grated Swiss Cheese, *2/3 c.*
Grated Parmesan Cheese, *1/3 c.*
Milk, *1 c.*
Eggs, *8-10 (about 1 1/2 cups)*
Salt, *1/2 t.*
Pepper, *to taste*

Serves 6-8.

Low in: **cal carb**

Wash and trim the broccoli and chop it coarsely. Use only the flowerets and the tender parts of stalks which have been peeled.　◆**C**ook the onions in 2 T. of the corn oil margarine until soft. Add chopped broccoli and stir. Cover, lower heat and cook slowly until broccoli is semi-soft (*al dente*).

◆**I**n a large mixing bowl, beat the eggs. Add the milk and cheese and blend well. Add broccoli, taking care to scrape all bits from pan into egg mixture.　◆**G**rease a large custard mold or soufflé dish with 1 T. of margarine and pour the batter into it.

◆**S**et the mold into a larger pan of boiling water (*bain-marie*) and place in a pre-heated 375° oven. Allow to bake for 35 to 40 minutes—or until center of custard is set. Let this dish "settle" for 15 minutes or so before cutting.

Chiles Rellenos Casserole

This is a short-form version of chiles rellenos, which gives you much of the eating pleasure without the fuss. The use of tofu instead of kidney beans reduces the carbohydrate content considerably — and the result is a simple-to-prepare and quite delicious eating experience.

Mash the tofu with the oil, chili powder and garlic. Place this, in a layer, on the bottom of a 2-quart casserole. ◆**A**dd half the peppers, distributing evenly. Add all the cheese, and cover with the remaining peppers. ◆**B**eat the egg whites until stiff. Beat the yolks and fold in the whites, along with the flour and baking powder. ◆**S**pread this mixture on top of the chili-cheese layers and bake for 30 to 40 minutes in a 350° oven until browned. May be served with a green taco or jalapeno sauce to add to the zest!

Serves 4-6.

Low in: **cal carb**

2 cakes of drained **Tofu**
(bean curd)
2 T. **Corn Oil**
2 t. **Chili Powder**
1 t. **Garlic Powder**
Green Ortega Chilis
2 small cans, chopped
3/4 lb. **Monterey Jack Cheese**
cut in 1/2" cubes
4, separated, **Eggs**
1 T. **Flour**
1 t. **Baking Powder**

Eggs 'n' Things
91

Green Peppers Costa Brava

Whew! Hot!
But totally wonderful . . .
green peppers, ortega chilis,
tofu and yogurt!
Zounds!

Onion, 1, *sliced thin*
Corn Oil, 2 T.
Green Peppers, 4, *cut into 1/4" strips*
Garlic, 2 *cloves, smashed*
Cumin, 1 T., *ground*
Coriander, 1 T., *ground*
Cayenne Pepper, 1/2 t.
Salt, 1/2 t.
Monterey Jack Cheese, 1/2 lb.
Green Ortega Chilis, 1 can
  cut in strips
Tofu *(bean curd), 1/2 lb.*
  drained and crumbled
Eggs, 2
Yogurt, 3/4 c.

Eggs
'n' Things
92

Sauté the onion slices in the corn oil, in a large frying pan. Add the peppers, garlic and all seasonings and stir-fry for about 10 minutes—until peppers begin to go soft. ◆ **P**our this mixture into an ungreased 9" pie plate and top with slices of Jack cheese and green chilis.
  ◆ **B**eat the eggs and beat in the crumbled tofu and the yogurt. Spread this "custard" over the pepper mixture.
◆ **B**ake in a pre-heated 375° oven for 45 minutes, or until custard in brown.

Serves 5-6.

Low in: **cal carb chol**

Eggplant San Miguel

This eggplant and tofu dish can become a substantial meatless main dish, or a savoury for a hot lunch or buffet supper. It is not too spicy, but it has a decided "kick."

Slice the eggplant, skin on, into 3/4" rounds. Place on a cookie sheet. With a pastry brush, brush each slice lightly with corn oil, then salt and pepper. Broil 2" from flame until nicely brown. Turn and broil the other side. ◆ **M**ake the tofu cream as follows: Drain the tofu in a colander for about 30 minutes. Pat it dry. Break it up in a bowl and add the rest of the ingredients. Blend well. ◆ **P**re-heat oven to 350°. ◆ **I**n a 3-quart casserole dish, spoon enough canned hot enchilada sauce (your favorite brand) to cover bottom. Then, make a layer of eggplant using one-half of the eggplant. ◆ **O**n top of the eggplant layer, place 1/2 of the tofu cream, the sliced Emmenthaler cheese, the rest of the sauce. Sprinkle the grated Parmesan over all. ◆ **N**ow use the remaining eggplant to make a second eggplant layer, and cover this with remaining tofu cream. ◆ **B**ake for 30 minutes. Allow the dish to cool for about 10 minutes before cutting.

Serves 5-6.

Low in: **cal carb chol**

1 large **Eggplant**
2 T. **Corn Oil**
1 12-oz. can **Hot Enchilada Sauce**
1/2 lb. sliced **Emmenthaler Cheese**
2 T. **Grated Parmesan Cheese**
Salt
Pepper

TOFU CREAM:

1 1/2 lb. **Tofu**
(bean curd)
8 oz. plain **Yogurt**
1/2 c. chopped **Green Onions**
1 1/2 t. **Salt**
to taste, **Pepper**
2 t. **Chili Powder**
1 t. ground **Cumin**

Frittata

Frittata, a variation of an omelet, is not recommended for serious cholesterol watchers. However, it makes a perfectly lovely light supper for other bulge-battlers. Vary the vegetables in frittata —or use left-over lean meat or poultry to smarten up the dish.

Eggs, *5*
Bread Crumbs, *1/4 c.*
Grated Parmesan Cheese, *3 T.*
Thyme, *1 t.*
Salt, *1/4 t.*
Pepper, *freshly ground, to taste*
Zucchini, **1 c. thinly sliced*
Corn Oil Margarine, *2 T.*

Beat the eggs until frothy. Add the bread crumbs, the cheese, the seasonings, the zucchini.　◆ In a large skillet, melt the margarine and heat until sizzling. Add the egg-zucchini mixture, pulling edges away from the sides of the pan with a fork, as the egg sets. When bottom is golden, cover the skillet with a flat lid or plate; turn upside down and slide frittata back into pan. (Whew!) Cook until golden, or until the egg is completely set. Serve immediately.

Serves 4-6.

*Use spinach, bean sprouts, tomato, leeks, mushrooms, etc. as alternatives to the zucchini in making frittata.

Low in: **cal carb**

Nirimish Vegetables

This cooked vegetable medley comes from a favorite restaurant—London's Ganges. If you are over there, and enjoy Indian food, it has my enthusiastic recommendation. While waiting for your trip to materialize, try Nirimish Vegetables at home. The secret is in the spicing.

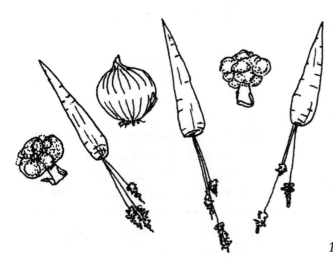

Heat oil in a large casserole pot and add seeds. Cover pan with lid as seeds will burst. After 30 seconds, remove lid, lower heat and add onions. Sauté until light brown.

◆ **Add** turmeric and salt. Add vegetables, starting with those which require more cooking first. Stir-fry for 3 to 4 minutes, stirring frequently.

◆ **Now** add tomatoes with juice from can and lemon juice. Cover and cook over low heat, for about 30 minutes.

Serves 4-6.

2 lbs. of **Fresh Vegetables,***
cut in coarse dice
l large, diced coarsely, **Onion**
1 28-oz. can **Stewed Tomatoes**
2 T. **Corn Oil**
1/2 t. ground **Turmeric**
1/2 t. whole **Mustard Seeds**
1/2 t. whole **Cumin Seeds**
1/2 t. whole **Coriander Seeds**
1 T. **Lemon Juice**
1/2 t. **Salt**

Eggs
'n' Things
95

**The vegetables for this dish may vary with the seasons, or with what is locally available. Try cauliflower, carrots, string beans, broccoli, zucchini, squash, potato, in any combinations you prefer.*

Low in: **cal carb chol**

Spinach with Feta Cheese & Dill

Spinach is probably the winning vegetable in offering the fewest calories and a good source of nutrition. It has found its way into many B-B recipes —and here is yet another, where it combines with feta cheese and dillweed. In addition to its other merits, it takes only minutes to prepare.

Spinach, *1 lb. fresh, washed and trimmed*
Feta Cheese, *1/4 lb., crumbled*
Dillweed, *1 t.*
Pepper, *freshly ground, to taste*

In a large saucepan, cook the spinach in its own water, for about 5 minutes. Pour into a colander and press out as much water as you can. Place spinach in a heat-proof dish.
◆ **B**lend the feta cheese, dillweed and pepper into the spinach and place in a pre-heated oven for about 10 minutes—just to warm through before serving.

Serves 3-4.

Low in: **cal carb chol**

Squash Pudding

Pattipan squash has a very short season where we live. But when I can get it, I like to turn it into this unexpected pudding, looking much like a potato pudding, but with less than 1/3 of the calories.

In a blender or food processor, purée the squash and onion. ◆ Pour the purée into a bowl. Beat in the 4 eggs, the garlic, bread crumbs, pepper and salt, the sage, and 2 tablespoons of the corn oil, and blend well. ◆ Pour the batter into a 9" deep pie dish or an 8" square baking dish which has been oiled with the remaining tablespoon of oil. Sprinkle paprika generously over the top. ◆ Bake in a pre-heated 350° oven for 45 minutes—or until nicely browned on top.

Serves 4-5.

Low in: **cal carb chol***
*less than 3/4 egg per 1/6 portion

2-3 lbs. **Pattipan Squash**
peeled and seeds removed
4 whole **Eggs**
1 **Onion**
1 large clove, smashed, **Garlic**
1/4 c. **Whole Wheat Bread Crumbs**
2 T. chopped fresh **Sage**
or 1 t. dried
3 T. **Corn Oil**
1/2 t. **Salt**
freshly ground, to taste, **Pepper**
Paprika

Tofu Salad

Tofu, that excellent addition to our diet, has many versatile qualities. In this simple salad, it is a swell and satisfying substitute for those who must shirk from eggs. Warning: it is HOT! (though you can make it less so . . .)

Tofu, *2 cakes, drained and mashed*
Green Onions, *6, chopped*
Garlic, *1 large clove, chopped*
Cilantro, *1 bunch, chopped*
Dijon Mustard, *2 T.*
Cumin Seeds, *1 T. whole*
Salt, *1/2 t. (or to taste)*
Green Chili Pepper, *1 seeded and chopped*
Peanut Butter, *1/3 c.*
Turmeric, *1 t. ground*

Place the mashed tofu in a bowl. Add green onions, garlic, cilantro, diced chili pepper and peanut butter and mix well.   ◆ **U**se a mortar and pestle or a blender to grind the cumin. (You can, of course, use already ground cumin, but the addition of freshly ground cumin makes a lot of difference.) Add the cumin, mustard, salt and turmeric. ◆ **C**hill and serve. This salad keeps for several days without losing its appeal.

Serves 4-6.

Low in: **cal carb chol**

Tofu Marsala with Mushrooms

Shivan Robinsong took the Veal Marsala recipe (see page 60) and substituted tofu for the meat. This delicious variation of that scrumptuous dish will make converts of even the most reluctant tofu-eater.

Roll each piece of tofu in the grated cheese. ◆ **In** a large, heavy skillet, heat the oil and sauté the tofu until lightly browned on both sides. Remove the tofu to a platter.
◆ **In** the same pan, sauté the mushrooms for 2 to 3 minutes. Remove them to the tofu platter. ◆ **T**o the juices in the pan add the Marsala, the onion soup mix, the Worcestershire sauce and the tamari. Add whatever bits of cheese are left from the 1/3 cup used for dipping the tofu. With a spatula, scrape bits and pieces from the bottom of the pan and blend all ingredients thoroughly.
◆ **R**aise heat and simmer sauce for 3 to 4 minutes. Return the tofu and mushrooms to the pan and turn gently in the sauce, so that all ingredients are blended. Serve immediately.

Serves 3-4.

Low in: **cal carb chol**

1 lb. pressed* **Tofu**
2 T. **Corn Oil**
1/2 lb., quartered, **Mushrooms**
1 T. **Onion Soup Mix**
1 t. **Worcestershire Sauce**
1 t. **Tamari Soya Sauce**
1/2 c. **Marsala**
1/3 c. **Grated Parmesan Cheese**

*Eggs
'n' Things*
99

*If you are unable to obtain pressed tofu, use regular tofu and (a) slice each cake into 1" pieces, (b) place on paper towels, on top of a newspaper; (c) place a board on top, with a 3 to 4 lb. weight on top of board; (d) leave for 1 to 2 hours. Voilà! Pressed tofu.

Tofu in an Indonesian Sauce

For the more adventurous eater, a quick to prepare, low cal-carb, & inexpensive dish, with a spicy Indonesian flavor. The faint-of-heart may wish to substitute plain green pepper for the chili pepper. But some like it hot. Handle chili peppers with respect!

Tofu, *2 8-oz. cakes*
Corn Oil, *2 T.*
Bay Leaf, *1*
Green Chili Pepper, *1*
  seeded and chopped
Water, *1 c.*
Onion Soup Mix, *2 t. dehydrated*
Ginger, *1/2 t.*
Peanut Butter, *4 T.*
Sambal Oelek, **1 t.*
Garlic, *2 cloves, smashed*
Onion, *1 medium, minced*
Salt, *1 t.*
Cilantro, *1 bunch, washed and chopped*
Vinegar, *1/4 c.*

Eggs
'n' Things
100

Put tofu in a colander and weigh it down by placing a heavy dish on top, to press out excess moisture. Press for at least 1 hour. Then, cut in cubes, about 2″ x 2″. ◆ **H**eat oil in a frying pan and sauté the onion and garlic for about 3 to 4 minutes. Add ginger, peanut butter, sambal and salt. Stir-fry for 1 minute. Add vinegar and work all ingredients into a paste. ◆ **A**dd the water, the bay leaf, the chili pepper and the dehydrated onion soup, and stir until thoroughly blended. ◆ **S**tir in the chunks of tofu, and simmer over low heat for about 10 minutes, stirring occasionally. ◆ **R**emove to a serving dish and sprinkly generously with fresh cilantro.

Serves 3-4.

*An Indonesian chili condiment available in most Chinese and Japanese groceries, as well as the more venturesome supermarkets.

Low in: **carb cal chol**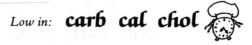

Eggplant Pâté

Here is an eggplant dish that makes a wonderful luncheon entrée —with a surprisingly new taste. It is incredibly easy, taking only moments in the preparation once the eggplant has been broiled.

Remove stem from eggplant & cut it in half, lengthwise. Prick skin all over with a fork. Place the two halves, cut-side down, on a baking tray and broil 2″ from element for 15 minutes. Skin will get quite scorched. ◆**W**hile eggplant is broiling, grind almonds in a food processor or blender. ◆**L**et eggplant cool. Scoop out flesh, discard skin, & purée meat in a blender or food processor. ◆**P**ut puréed eggplant in a bowl & combine with ground almonds, mayonnaise, lemon juice, garlic, salt, ginger & pepper. Mix well. Chill & serve.

Serves 3-4.

1 (about 1 lb. size) **Eggplant**
2/3 c. ground, toasted unblanched **Almonds**
1 T. **Mayonnaise**
2 T. **Lemon Juice**
1 clove, crushed, **Garlic**
1/4 t. **Salt**
1/2 t. ground **Ginger**
1/8 t. **Pepper**

Low in: **cal carb chol**

Eggs 'n' Things
101

Spaghetti Squash

This amazing vegetable is a product of some botanist's creative genius. In the low-cal squash department, it shreds into spaghetti-like strands after cooking — so that bulge battlers may indulge spaghetti tastes on a squash budget. Fall in love with this vegetable in the produce section of your local market.

Spaghetti Squash, *1*
Corn Oil Margarine, *2 T.*
Grated Parmesan Cheese, *1/2 c.*
Salt, *1/2 t.*
Basil, *1 T. dried*
Garlic, *2 large cloves, smashed*

Cut the squash in half, lengthwise, and carefully scoop out and discard the seeds. ◆ **P**lace on a baking tray and bake in a pre-heated 350° oven for 40 minutes. Allow to cool somewhat, until it is easy to handle. Then, with a fork or large spoon, scoop out all the strands of squash—down to the very skin—and place in a vegetable dish. ◆ **M**ix the cheese, salt, basil and mashed garlic thoroughly with the squash. Dot the top with margarine and place under broiler for a few moments, until heated throughout. Serve hot.

Serves 4-6.

Low in: **cal carb chol**

VEGETABLE ACCOMPANIMENTS

Broccoli Romano

Of the many and varied ways to prepare this excellent vegetable, this harmony of lemon and garlic is surely in the top ten.

Broccoli, *1 bunch*
Salt, *1/4 t.*
Corn Oil Margarine, *2 T.*
Garlic, *2 cloves, smashed*
Mustard Powder, *1 t.*
Grated Lemon Rind, *1 T.*
Lemon, *juice of 1*

Vegetables

◆

104

Wash the broccoli and trim the stalks. Peel the tender parts of the stalks, and cut these, along with the flowerets, into 1" pieces. ◆ **C**ook the broccoli in lightly salted water for 6 to 7 minutes, or until medium tender. (Do not overcook, or you will lose flavor, texture and nutrients.) Drain and place in a heated vegetable dish. ◆ **I**n a small saucepan, combine the margarine and garlic, and heat to a simmer. Add the mustard powder, lemon rind and lemon juice and stir until thoroughly blended. ◆ **P**our this warm sauce over the broccoli and serve immediately.

Serves 4-5.

Low in: **cal carb chol**

Broccoli
Sauté *For garlic lovers only!*

Wash and trim ends of broccoli. Peel the tender parts of the stalks and cut these on the diagonal into pieces—each about 3″ long, and not too thick.   ◆**In** a large frying pan, heat the oil and stir-fry the garlic for a few minutes. ◆**Add** the broccoli (this will splatter), salt, and stir. Cover pan, lower heat and cook for 7 to 8 minutes, or until broccoli is *al dente* (medium tender). Shake pan several times during cooking.

Serves 4-5.

Low in: **cal carb chol**

1 bunch **Broccoli**
3-4 cloves, cut in chunks, **Garlic**
3 T. **Corn Oil**
1/2 t. **Salt**

Vegetables
◆
105

Cabbage Sauté

Don't turn your nose up at cabbage —first try this dish. It may become your new favorite vegetable accompaniment.

Cabbage, 1 small head, shredded
Onion, 1 large, sliced thin
Caraway Seeds, 1 T.
Paprika, 2 T.
Salt, 1/2 t.
Corn Oil, 3 T.

Vegetables
◆
106

Sauté the onion in the oil in a large frying pan for about 5 minutes, or until just soft. ◆**A**dd cabbage. Cover pan, lower heat and cook for 10 minutes. This will reduce bulk of cabbage and enable you now to stir it through. ◆**A**dd remainder of ingredients and stir through once again. Continue cooking, covered, for about 20 minutes more, stirring occasionally. Serve warm.

Serves 5-6.

Low in: **cal carb chol**

Cauliflower Sauté

Here's an interesting new way to prepare that great, low-calorie standard, cauliflower, in a manner that will impress even the most discriminating eaters. Low in calories, cholesterol and carbohydrates, simple to prepare—and incredibly delicious. What more can you ask!

In a large frying pan (with a fitted cover), sauté the onion and garlic in the oil until they are quite brown.　◆**A**dd the pieces of cauliflower, the salt and pepper and continue the sauté, stirring, for about 2 minutes more.　◆**A**dd the vinegar, blend well, and cover. Lower heat and steam for about 8 minutes.　◆**R**emove cover, turn up heat and cook quickly to reduce liquid. Cauliflower can be served at this point. Or, if you want to gussy it up a bit, go on to the next step.　◆**T**ransfer the cauliflower to a baking dish. Top with grated Swiss cheese and place under a pre-heated broiler until brown on top.

Serves 4-5.

Low in: **cal carb chol**

1 large, diced fine, **Onion**
1 large clove, diced, **Garlic**
2 T. **Corn Oil**
1 medium size head **Cauliflower**
broken into small-sized flowerets
1/2 t. **Salt**
freshly ground, to taste, **Pepper**
1/3 c. **White Vinegar**
1/3 c. **Grated Swiss Cheese**
(optional)

Vegetables
◆
107

Sautéed Kale

This is a variation of sautéed broccoli and will come as a surprise to those who think of kale as only a decoration.

In a large frying pan, heat oil and fry garlic pieces for a few minutes, until they just begin to take on some color.
◆**A**dd kale and stir so that the oil touches most of the vegetable. Cover the pan, lower heat and fry for 10 to 12 minutes, or until the kale is dark and the stalk parts are tender. Serve immediately.

Serves 3-4.

Kale, *1 bunch*
   trimmed, washed & cut in large pieces
Corn Oil, *3 T.*
Garlic, *3-4 large cloves, cut in slivers*

Low in: **cal carb chol**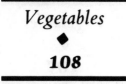

Vegetables
◆
108

Artichokes in Garlic, Oil & Vinegar

Artichokes simmered whole in a garlic, oil and vinegar marinade may come as an appetizer, or as an accompaniment to an entrée.

Place the artichokes stem side up in a large saucepan. Add the remaining ingredients to the pan. ◆**C**over the pan and bring to a boil. Reduce heat and simmer until the stem of the artichoke feels soft when pierced with a fork—about 20 minutes. ◆**R**emove from marinade and drain. These artichokes may be served hot, and they are equally delicious cold.

Serves 4.

Low in: **cal carb chol**

4, washed and trimmed, **Artichokes**
3 large cloves, sliced, **Garlic**
2 T. **Corn Oil**
1/4 c. **White Vinegar**
1 qt. **Water**
1/4 t. **Salt**

Vegetables
◆
109

Spinach with Yogurt & Garlic

The idea of combining yogurt with spinach was handed down to us from the Middle East. They had a great idea.

Spinach, *2 bunches fresh washed and trimmed*
Garlic, *2 cloves, cut in small pieces*
Yogurt, *1/2 c. plain*

Vegetables
◆
110

Cook spinach in a covered saucepan, adding no water other than what is already on the leaves from washing. This should take no more than 5 minutes. ◆**D**rain the spinach thoroughly and while in colander, make several cuts through with sharp knife. ◆**R**eturn to saucepan. Add garlic and yogurt and stir. Heat until just warm (do not cook) and serve immediately.

Serves 4-5.

Low in: **cal carb chol**

Butternut Squash & Cinnamon

This is so easy to prepare and so delicious, you will want to make it a regular in your menu plans.

Peel the squash and cut it into chunks. Place in saucepan, cover with water, add salt. Cover and cook until soft— about 10 minutes. ◆ **D**rain thoroughly and mash with a potato masher. ◆ **T**ransfer to a deep vegetable dish and mix in the corn oil margarine. Smooth over the top with a spatula and sprinkle the cinnamon over the top. ◆ **P**lace in a pre-heated 350° oven for about 5 minutes, so that it is thoroughly warmed. Serve immediately.

Serves 4-5.

Low in: **cal carb chol**

2 lbs. **Yellow Squash**
(butternut or hubbard)
2 T. **Corn Oil Margarine**
2 t. **Cinnamon**
1/2 t. **Salt**

Vegetables
◆
111

Jack's Gingery Carrots

When Jack experiments in the kitchen, watch out! This time he came up with a carrot-ginger combination that adds nobility to this familiar vegetable. A wonderful accompaniment to any entrée.

Carrots, *3 c.*
Dehydrated Onion Flakes, *1/4 c.*
Corn Oil Margarine, *2 T.*
Ginger, *1 t. (heaping) ground*
Mustard Powder, *1/2 t.*

Vegetables
◆
112

Trim and scrape the carrots and cut them in julienne.
◆ **In** a large saucepan, sauté the dehydrated onion in the corn oil margarine until soft. This goes rather quickly, so it is best that you watch over it.
◆ **A**dd the carrots, ginger and mustard and toss thoroughly. Lower the heat, cover and cook until carrots are done.*

Serves 4-5.

Some people prefer the carrots quite soft. We like them "al dente"—so that they still retain just a bit of their natural crunchy texture.

Low in: **cal carb chol**

Carrots Lyonnaise

Carrots cooked in their own juices, with a sprinkling of thyme, makes an elegant taste treat in this vegetable accompaniment to a meat or fish entrée.

Melt margarine in a saucepan. Add onion and sauté, on medium heat, for about 5 minutes, until soft. ◆ **A**dd carrots, thyme, salt and pepper and stir until all ingredients are blended. Cover, lower heat, and cook until carrots are tender, stirring occasionally.

Serves 4-5.

Low in: **cal carb chol**

2 T. **Corn Oil Margarine**
1/2 c. chopped **Onion**
3 c. sliced **Carrots**
1 t. **Thyme**
1/4 t. **Salt**
dash of ground **Black Pepper**

Vegetables
◆
113

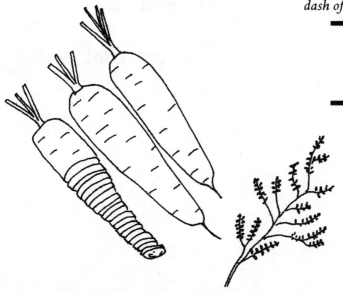

Sautéed Turnips

What —me eat turnips?
That underrated vegetable
takes on new meaning
when sautéed
and sprinkled with nutmeg.

Turnips, *2 lbs. (white or yellow)*
peeled and cut into chunks
Corn Oil Margarine, *2 T.*
Salt, *1/4 t.*
Nutmeg, *1/2 t.*

Melt the corn oil margarine in a large skillet with a cover. Add the turnips, salt and nutmeg and stir through, so that each piece of turnip has a light coating of margarine.
◆ **C**over the pan, reduce the heat and cook slowly until the turnips are soft when pierced with a fork. Stir occasionally during cooking time to prevent scorching.

Serves 4-5.

Low in: **cal chol carb**

Baked Acorn Squash

Acorn squash, which is naturally sweet, needs no added sweetener when it is baked with cinnamon and corn oil margarine. This is probably one of the easiest recipes to prepare; the time it requires to bake, however, prevents it from earning the "chef's clock" symbol.

2 **Acorn Squash**
cut in half, with seeds removed
2 T. **Corn Oil Margarine**
2 t. **Cinnamon**

Vegetables
◆
115

Pre-heat oven to 350°. Place squash on a shallow baking dish, cut side up. ◆ **P**lace bits of the margarine into the cavity of the squash and sprinkle with cinnamon.

◆ **B**ake for about 1 hour, or until the flesh is quite soft.
Serves 4-6.

Low in: **cal carb chol**

Zucchini Genovese

This absolutely divine zucchini with a pesto-type flavoring is one of my very favorite all-time vegetable recipes.

Zucchini, *2 lbs., washed and trimmed*
Oil, *2 T.*
Corn Oil Margarine, *2 T.*
Salt, *1/2 t.*
Grated Parmesan Cheese, *1/2 c.*
Basil, *1/2 c., chopped fresh (or 2 T. dried)*
Black Pepper, *freshly ground*
Garlic, *2 cloves, smashed*

Vegetables
◆
116

Grate zucchini coarsely. (A food processor will do this nicely, if you have one.) Place in a colander, sprinkle with salt and let drain for at least 30 minutes. ◆**H**eat the margarine with the oil in a large skillet, over moderate heat. Add the zucchini. Season with pepper and shake the pan, tossing zucchini so it cooks evenly. Do this for 2 to 3 minutes. Do not overcook zucchini. It should retain some of its crispness. ◆**T**urn into a heatproof vegetable dish and add basil and garlic, mixing them through with a fork. If any liquid accumulates, pour it off. ◆**S**prinkle grated Parmesan cheese all over the top of the zucchini and place under a pre-heated broiler flame for about 5 minutes—or until the cheese turns crusty on top.

Serves 4-6.

Low in: **cal carb chol**

Two Standard Preparations for Vegetables

These two "standard" sauces —the first with a pair of variations — will enhance many different vegetable types.

1 LEMON "BUTTER" SAUCE

juice of 1 **Lemon**
1 T. **Grated Lemon Rind**
2 T. **Corn Oil Margarine**

Heat these together for just moments to produce a quick, light and flavorful sauce for vegetables. ◆*Variation I:* Add a clove of garlic, smashed, to the sauce, for a garlickly highlight. ◆*Variation II:* Add 1 t. mustard powder, if you like a sauce with some added "zing."

Any of the following vegetables, steamed, or cooked in lightly salted water, will take very kindly to this treatment: broccoli, asparagus, brussel sprouts, cauliflower, green beans, leeks, fresh peas, snow peas.

2 "BUTTER" AND PARMESAN

2 T. **Corn Oil Margarine,** *melted*
2 T. **Grated Parmesan Cheese**

Pour the melted margarine over the vegetable and sprinkle with the grated cheese.

This second preparation will go well with cooked vegetables that like to combine with cheese. Some examples: cauliflower, broccoli, fennel, brussel sprouts, spinach, tomatoes.

Low in: **cal carb chol**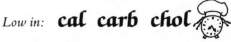

Vegetable Medley Sauté

This Buddha's feast is made with whatever vegetables are fresh and in season, so take a risk, be inventive, and create your own combinations. The medley below is one way to play it out.

Mushrooms, *1/2 fresh cleaned and quartered*
Onion, *1, in chunks*
Garlic, *2 cloves*
Celery, *3/4 stalks*
Green Pepper, *1*
Chinese Black Mushrooms, *3-4 dried*
Water Chestnuts, *1 can drained and sliced*
Broccoli, *2 stalks, trimmed and cut up*
Corn Oil, *3 T.*
Salt, *1/2 t.*
Pepper, *freshly ground, to taste*
Soya Sauce, *1 T.*
Mustard Powder, *1 t.*
Ginger, *1 t. ground*

Vegetables

◆

118

Begin by soaking the dried mushrooms in very hot water, for about 30 minutes. When they are soft, drain them well and cut them into thin strips.
◆ **H**eat the oil in a large frying pan. Add the onions and garlic and sauté for abut 5 minutes, or until soft.   ◆ **A**dd broccoli, green pepper and celery. Stir round and cover. Lower heat and cook for 5 minutes more.   ◆ **A**dd mushrooms (both kinds) and water chestnuts. Cover. Cook for 5 minutes more.   ◆ **A**dd all seasonings and stir through. Raise heat, uncover, and keep stirring until all ingredients are thoroughly mixed. Serve immediately. Vegetables should be crisp.

Serves 4-6.

Low in: **cal carb chol**

Cheese Crusted Tomatoes

This variation of Tomatoes Provençale takes only moments to prepare and is an easy, low-cal and low-carb addition to your dinner.

Place the tomatoes, cut side up, on a small broiler pan.
◆ **M**ix the cheese, oregano, basil and pepper together and sprinkle over the cut surface of the tomato. ◆ **P**lace a dot of the margarine on each and put under a pre-heated broiler for about 3 to 5 minutes—or until the cheese is brown and crusty. Serve at once.

Serves 4.

Low in: **cal carb chol**

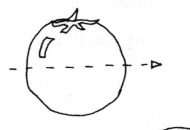

FIRM Tomatoes
4, cut in half cross-wise
2 T. **Grated Parmesan Cheese**
1/2 t. **Oregano**
1/2 t. **Basil**
freshly ground **Pepper**
8 small dots of **Corn Oil Margarine**
(about 1/2 t. each)

Vegetables
◆
119

Roasted Vegetables

Several vegetables, other than potatoes, take kindly to oven-roasting. They may be added to the pan of a roasting chicken or turkey, or roasted with a little corn oil margarine. They make a lovely color group in the pan, and give eating variety. The preparation is simple! Only the roasting takes time.

Vegetables suitable for roasting:

Carrots
Eggplant
Jerusalem Artichokes
   (unbelievably scrumptuous)
Parsnips
Squash *of all kinds*
Turnips
Rutabagas

Vegetables
◆
120

Pre-heat the oven to 350°.
◆ **P**eel the vegetables and cut into chunks. These need not be too small.   ◆ **I**f you are roasting the vegetables solo, put the margarine into the roasting pan, and put pan in the oven for a few moments to allow the margarine to melt. Remove.   ◆ **S**catter the vegetables in the pan, and turn them around in the melted margarine. Roast for about 1 hour.

Low in: **cal carb chol**

DESSERTS

Frozen Strawberry & Banana Yogurt

These are best made if you own an ice-cream maker. Using fruit to sweeten, plus a small quantity of fructose, will definitely satisfy your sweet tooth and hold down the calorie count.

Sprinkle the gelatin over the water and let stand for 5 minutes. Then stir over low heat until gelatin is completely dissolved. ◆ **In** a blender, combine the berries, the banana, the gelatin mixture, the fructose and the almond extract and purée. ◆ **If** you are using eggs (for a richer yogurt), beat them until thick and pale yellow. Stir into berry mixture. ◆ **S**tir yogurt into berry mixture and pour into the ice-cream maker. Follow the manufacturer's directions for freezing ice-cream, for the yogurt.

Serves 4-6.

*Other combinations of fruits, or fruits and nuts, will also make for happy frozen yogurt desserts. Try: banana and chopped almonds; raspberry and banana; raspberry and apple; peach and almonds.

Low in: **cal chol**

1 package unflavored **Gelatin**
2 c. frozen, unsweetened **Strawberries***
1 ripe **Banana**
1/3 c. **Fructose**
1/2 t. **Almond Extract**
(optional) 2 **Eggs**
2 c. plain **Yogurt**
1/4 c. **Water**

Desserts

◆

123

Fruited Yogurt Desserts

These are simple to prepare and are equally delicious. Here are variations on a theme. But do use fresh fruits in season.

All four preparations are similar: ◆ **P**urée in a blender or food processor. ◆ **A**dd the yogurt and mix thoroughly. Chill and serve.

Serves 4-6.

Low in: **cal chol**

Desserts

◆

124

VARIATION 1: Prince's Passion

2 c. fresh or frozen **Strawberries**
2 large, ripe **Bananas**
1 t. **Almond Extract**
3 c. plain, unflavored **Yogurt**

VARIATION 2: Queen's Fancy

3 ripe **Pears,** *peeled, cut up*
1 ripe **Banana**
1 t. **Vanilla**
1 T. **Honey**
3 c. plain **Yogurt**

VARIATION 3: King's Favorite

2 c. **Blueberries**
4 ripe **Peaches,** *peeled, cut up*
1 t. **Almond Extract**
1 T. **Honey**
1/4 c. **Triple Sec**
1 c. chopped **Almonds**
3 c. plain **Yogurt**

VARIATION 4: Emperor's Delight

3 juicy **Apples,** *peeled, cut up*
1/2 c. toasted **Almonds**
1 T. **Honey**
1/2 t. **Cinnamon**
1/2 t. **Nutmeg**
3 c. plain **Yogurt**

Apple Soufflé

This apple soufflé dessert is not a soufflé, strictly speaking—it's certainly not as finicky to produce—but its superior flavor and its light texture make it an excellent finale to a large dinner.

Peel, core and cut apples. Poach them in the vermouth and water, with the cinnamon stick, the cloves, the lemon, orange and margarine, until soft. ◆ **R**emove the spices and the slices of lemon and orange and purée the apples. ◆ **A**dd the walnuts and the liqueur and blend thoroughly. This dessert may be served warm or cold.

Serves 4-6.

Low in: **cal chol**

6-8 large **Apples**
1 c. **Dry White Vermouth**
1/2 c. **Water**
1 **Cinnamon Stick**
8 **Cloves**
3 slices **Lemon**
4 slices **Orange**
2 T. **Corn Oil Margarine**
1/2 c. chopped **Walnuts**
1/4 c. **Grand Marnier**
or **Cointreau**

Desserts

◆

125

Apple Strudel

The natural sweetness of apples makes it possible to eliminate the sugar from this very favorite dessert without sacrificing flavor. This recipe makes about six strudels. If you eat them all in one sitting, the calories consumed will be outrageous. If you restrict yourself to one slice after dinner, the total cost to waistline is considerably less than most other desserts or even strudels.

Filo Dough, *1/2 lb.*
Corn Oil Margarine, *1/2 lb., melted*
Apples, *1 dozen delicious peeled, cored and cut into chunks*
Raisins, *1 c.*
Walnuts, *1 c.*
Cinnamon, *2 t.*
Nutmeg, *1 t.*

Desserts

◆

126

---

*Working with filo dough can be intimidating for the novice chef. The secret, however, is to make sure that when you are handling 1 set of filo sheets, the rest of the sheets are covered with a damp cloth. If the filo is allowed to dry out, you will find it crumbling under your touch and your strudel will end up in disaster city.

Combine apples, raisins, walnuts, cinnamon & nutmeg in a bowl. ◆ **P**lace 1 sheet of filo dough* on a dishtowel. With a pastry brush, brush some margarine lightly over it. Place another sheet on top & repeat margarine. Do this twice more, so that you have 4 sheets of filo dough in all (4 for 1 strudel). ◆ **P**lace about 1/6 of apple mixture in a long trail along top of filo stack —so that it does not quite reach the outer edges. ◆ **U**sing the dish towel, roll filo down from top, to form strudel. ◆ **L**ine a cookie sheet with parchment paper & place strudel on it, seam side down. Brush top with more melted margarine. ◆ **D**o this with remaining filo dough & apple mixture. You should have about 6 strudels. ◆ **B**ake in a pre-heated 375° oven for 30 to 40 minutes, or until brown on top.

Low in: **cal chol**

Oatmeal Cookies

The oatmeal and wheat germ add nutritional value, and the sugar has been eliminated from these delicious crunchy cookies. Again, if you are going to eat the whole lot in 1 sitting, you are in for a real bulge experience. But if you ration yourself to 1-2 cookies for dessert, they will quite easily fall into the range of calorie- and cholesterol-controlled dessert treats.

Cream margarine until very soft. (A mixer will do it nicely.) ◆**A**dd honey, vanilla, oatmeal, wheat germ, non-fat milk & chopped walnuts, & blend mixture thoroughly. It will be somewhat stiff. ◆**D**rop by teaspoonfuls onto a cookie sheet lined with parchment paper & press each cookie down so it is relatively flat & round. Bake in a pre-heated 350° oven for 15 minutes or until brown.

ca. 30 cookies

Low in: **cal chol**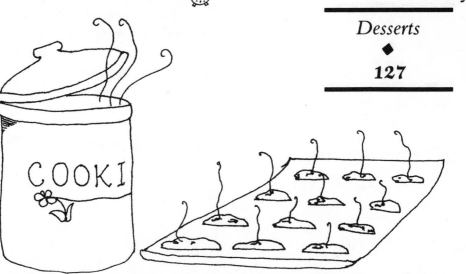

1/2 lb. **Corn Oil Margarine**
3 c. **Oatmeal**
1/2 c. **Wheat Germ**
3 t. **Vanilla**
3 T. **Non-fat Milk Powder**
1/2 c., chopped fine, **Walnuts**
1/2 c. **Honey**

Desserts
◆
127

Dynamite Crustless Fruit Pie

You can use almost any combination of fruit in this pie, but the one I like best is peach and blueberry, making it a summer-only treat. Easy-as-pie to prepare; only the baking time keeps this recipe from getting the "chef's clock" indicator.

Corn Oil Margarine, *7 T.*
Fresh Peaches
Fresh Blueberries
  combined to make up 4 generous cups
Flour, *3 T.*
Lemon, *juice of 1/2*
  grated rind of 1/2
Cinnamon, *2 t.*
Nutmeg, *1/2 t.*
Honey, *3 T.*
Rolled Oats, *2 c.*
Almonds, *1/2 c. chopped*
Salt, *1/2 t.*

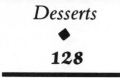

Desserts

♦

128

Grease a 9" pie plate with 1 T. corn oil margarine. ♦ Slice, but do not skin the peaches. Mix the fruit with 1 T. flour, lemon juice, lemon rind, 1 t. cinnamon and nutmeg. Pour into prepared pie plate. ♦ Melt 6 T. corn oil margarine with the honey. Mix this with the rolled oats, 1 t. cinnamon, chopped almonds, 2 T. flour and salt. ♦ Spread oat mixture over fruit evenly and press it into place. Bake in a preheated 400° oven for 35 to 40 minutes.

Low in: **cal chol**

Rose Kaye's Apple Crunch Pie

Rose Kaye, an ardent nutritionist, developed this "sugar-free" dessert for her family. Once again —if you eat the whole pie in one sitting, the result will be intense bulging. Eaten circumspectly, this dessert is within the limits of bulge-battling treats.

Peel the apples, core them, and cut them into chunks. Then poach them in a large saucepan, in about 1/2 c. water, with 1 cinnamon stick and 6 whole cloves, until the apples are very soft. Mash them with a potato masher, or wooden spoon. Remove the cinnamon and cloves and set the apple mash aside to cool.
◆ **M**elt the margarine in a frying pan and sauté the oatmeal for 5 minutes, stirring all the while. ◆ **M**ix the flour, wheat germ and cinnamon together and add to the oatmeal. Stir in the honey and blend all ingredients together thoroughly. ◆ **G**rease 2 9" pie plates with corn oil margarine and spread 1/4 of the crust mix in each. Press down to cover bottom and sides evenly. Add 1/2 of the applesauce to each and top with the rest of the crust mix.
◆ **B**ake for 30 minutes in a pre-heated 400° oven, or until the crust is nicley browned on top.

Makes 2 pies.

Low in: **cal chol**

THE CRUST:

1/2 lb. **Corn Oil Margarine**
3 c. **Oatmeal**
2/3 c. **Graham Flour**
1/2 c. **Honey**
2/3 c. **Wheat Germ**
1 t. **Cinnamon**

THE SAUCE:

8 large **Apples**
(delicious, winesap, granny smith, but not macintosh),
1 **Cinnamon Stick**
6 whole **Cloves**

Desserts
◆
129

Ricotta Torte

Easy, easy, easy to prepare, the orange and lemon zest give this torte its special quality.

Ricotta Cheese
  2 500-ml. containers
Flour, 3 T.
Honey, 1/4 c.
Eggs, 5, separated
Orange, grated rind of 1
Lemon, grated rind of 1
Marsala Wine 2 T. (or 2 t. vanilla)
Currants, 1/4 c.
Almonds, 1/2 c. chopped, toasted
  unblanched
Cinnamon, 2 t.
Corn Oil Margarine, 1 T.

Desserts

◆

130

Combine the cheese, flour, honey, egg yolks, rinds and wine (or vanilla) in the large bowl of an electric mixer and beat for 6 to 8 minutes. ◆**A**dd currants and nuts and mix well. ◆**B**eat the egg whites until stiff and fold them gently into the batter. ◆**G**rease a 9″ spring-form pan with the margarine and dust lightly with flour, tapping out excess. Turn batter into pan and sprinkle top with cinnamon. ◆**B**ake in a pre-heated 375° oven for about 45 minutes—or until nicely browned on top.

Low in: **cal carb**

Strawberry Cheesecake

This is a light, fruity cheesecake that will make a swell calorie-controlled dessert. The use of cottage cheese instead of cream cheese puts it also within reach of cholesterol counters.

This step is crucial: Drain excess liquid from the cottage cheese thoroughly by placing in a colander with a heavy weight on top for at least 30 minutes. If you don't, you will have cheesecake soup!
◆ **C**ombine cottage cheese, buttermilk, skim milk powder, whole eggs, lemon rind, honey and vanilla in a blender and purée until smooth.
◆ **A**dd puréed strawberries and mix thoroughly into cheese batter.   ◆ **C**arefully fold in beaten egg whites.
◆ **T**urn batter into a springform pan which has been greased with corn oil margarine, and bake in a preheated 350° oven for 40 minutes.

2 c. **Cottage Cheese**
1/3 c. **Buttermilk**
1/3 c. **Skim Milk Powder**
2 **Eggs**
grated rind of 1 **Lemon**
1/3 c. **Honey**
1 t. **Vanilla**
5, beaten stiff, **Egg Whites**
1 pt. puréed **Strawberries**
(unsweetened)
1 T. **Corn Oil Margarine**

Desserts

◆

131

Low in: **cal carb chol***
*less than 1/6 egg yolk in one serving

Cheesecake Sublime

This calorie-controlled cheesecake depends upon its mystery ingredient: banana —*which both naturally sweetens and gives it its incredibly wonderful taste. It is also simple to prepare. What more can you ask?*

Farmers Cheese, * *2 lbs.*
Eggs, *5*
Yogurt, *1 c.*
Honey, *1/3 c.*
Vanilla, *2 t.*
Almonds, *1/2 c. chopped, unblanched*
Lemon, *grated rind of 1*
Lemon, *juice of 1/2*
Salt, *1/4 t.*
Bananas, *2 ripe*
Corn Oil Margarine, *2 T.*

Desserts

◆

132

Place all ingredients except the almonds in a blender and purée for about 5 minutes, or until the batter is perfectly smooth. If your blender is like mine and holds only a quart, you may have to do this in two batches.   ◆ **G**rease a spring-form pan generously with the corn oil margarine and pour batter into it. Sprinkle chopped almonds lightly on top.
◆ **P**re-heat the oven to 375°. Place a pan of water on the bottom shelf of the oven. Bake the cheesecake on the middle shelf for 1 hour.   ◆ **R**emove and cool on a rack. But be sure to place a dish underneath the rack to catch the dripping-out of excess moisture during the cooling. The cheesecake may be served warm, or cold.

Farmers cheese is a dry form of cottage cheese available in many eastern cities and it is delicious in this cake, if you can get it. If not, cottage cheese, which has been drained overnight in cheesecloth, and then squeezed of every drop of excess moisture, is a reliable substitute.

Low in: **cal chol**

Indexes

A General Index begins on page 136.

(continued)

134

(continued)

(continued)